More Times and Places

William S. Gray, Marion Monroe,
A. Sterl Artley, May Hill Arbuthnot

SCOTT, FORESMAN AND COMPANY

Chicago, Atlanta, Dallas, Palo Alto, New York

Stories

Young Citizens Here and There

The Great Outdoors

Famous Americans of Other Times

Old Tales from Everywhere

Young Citizens
Here and There

Unwelcome Passengers

Penny and Peter were sitting on the dock near their seaside cottage. It was easy to see how Penny got his name. In the brilliant sunshine his hair shone like a new penny.

"It seems funny not to be out sailing on the last day of our vacation," he remarked.

"I know," said his brother Peter. "But Father put the sailboat away before he left. I wish he hadn't had to leave early."

After lunch the boys would be returning to the city with their mother. But now they did not know what to do with themselves.

Finally Peter had an idea. "Let's take the rowboat," he said. "Let's get some crabs and surprise Mother. Maybe we can have them for lunch."

"Oh, yes!" cried Penny. "I love crabs. But we must catch some fish for bait first."

After getting their fishing lines, the boys caught several fish at the end of the dock. Then they rowed out a short distance in the shallow water and sat motionless in the boat, waiting for crabs. They waited a long time. Finally Penny sighed impatiently.

"There don't seem to be any crabs today," he grumbled.

"Sometimes they all come at once," Peter said. "Let's wait a little longer."

7

Suddenly the shallow water by the rowboat was full of crabs. Peter grabbed a small net and scooped up a crab that was nibbling at the bait tied on his line.

"Got one!" he shouted. "A big one!"

"Me, too!" cried Penny. "Quick, get it!"

Peter scooped up crabs as fast as he could and dropped them into a basket in the boat.

"Aren't they beauties!" exclaimed Penny. "And won't Mother be surprised to see us bringing home crabs for lunch!"

Peter glanced at the cottage. "Look," he said, frowning. "It's too late to cook the crabs for lunch. Mother's already put out the time-to-eat signal. The old red sweater is hanging on the porch."

Penny's face clouded with disappointment. Then it brightened. "We might take the crabs back to town with us," Penny suggested. "I do hate to waste these crabs."

Peter guided the rowboat up to the dock. After tying the boat securely, the boys lifted out the bushel basket of crabs and carried it across the beach to the house.

"Hi, Mother!" cried Penny. "Look at the beautiful crabs we caught. Almost fifty."

"My goodness!" said his mother. "What shall we do with all those crabs? We are leaving on the two o'clock train."

"Why not take them home with us?" asked Peter. "We could keep them in this basket with some seaweed over them."

"Oh, no," said his mother. "You can't take animals in passenger cars."

"But that rule is for pets," argued Peter. "These crabs aren't pets. They're food."

"Well, can I depend on you boys to take charge of them?" asked their mother. "I've a shopping bag full of odds and ends that I want to take. With the bag and the suitcase, I can't handle anything more."

"We'll take care of the crabs all right," promised the boys.

After a hasty sandwich lunch, the family waited near the door for a taxicab to take them to the train. The boys' mother looked doubtfully at her shopping bag. It was full of half-used packages of flour, salt, tea, and other things. Sticking out of the bag were a pancake turner and a big cooking spoon.

"I hate to take all these things on the train," she said. "But I don't like to leave anything behind that I can use at home."

When the taxi came, everyone piled in.

"You're sure you have plenty of seaweed on the crabs, Peter?" asked his mother.

"Oh, sure, sure," Peter said as he looked at the basket on his lap.

When the taxicab arrived at the station, the train was already there. It was hard to get the heavy basket up the train steps, but the boys finally managed it.

Their mother led the way to a couple of vacant seats facing each other near one end of the car. She put the shopping bag and the suitcase on the shelf for baggage.

"Now, boys," she said, "you'll have to put the basket of crabs on the floor. Just do the best you can with your feet and legs. After all, the crabs were your idea."

As Penny and Peter lowered the crabs to the floor, the train started with a jerk. Penny dropped his end of the basket, and the basket promptly tipped over.

Then what excitement there was! Nearly all the crabs and seaweed spilled out into the aisle. The crabs began scrambling off in every direction. Bits of damp seaweed were still clinging to them.

"E-e-e-e-k!" squealed a frightened woman. "That seaweed's alive! It's walking!"

"No, it isn't!" shrieked another woman. "I mean it's crabs! Watch out!"

Children screamed. Some people began to jump up on the seats. Others blocked the aisle as they ran from the scurrying crabs.

Peter righted the basket. Penny cried, "Oh, Mother! Oh, Mother! Oh, Mother!"

"Stop moaning and do something," said his mother. "Get me that shopping bag."

She pulled the pancake turner out of the shopping bag and went after a nearby crab. She scooped it up, but it slid off.

Meanwhile, the other crabs were getting farther and farther away. Everyone in the car was either standing or kneeling on the seats. They were all watching the crabs.

"I need the big cooking spoon, too," said the boys' mother. "Hand it to me, Peter."

Peter handed her the spoon. She put the pancake turner under one crab and the big spoon on top of it. Then she was able to lift the crab back into the basket.

She started to go after another crab, but Peter, looking rather ashamed, stopped her. "Penny and I will get them, Mother. We said we'd take care of the crabs."

The two boys went crawling up and down the aisle. Peter had the pancake turner in one hand and the big spoon in the other. As Penny chased the crabs out from under the seats, Peter went after them. Frequently the crabs slid off the pancake turner before Peter could capture them with the big spoon. But by the time the train was halfway home, all the crabs were back in the basket.

"Well!" cried Peter as he sank down into his seat. "Now I know why there's a rule against taking animals in passenger cars."

"Me, too," said Penny wearily. "But I'm glad we didn't lose those crabs. I do love crabs—cooked ones, I mean."

A Christmas to Remember

It was a few days before Christmas. But as Jane Wallace swept the ranch-house porch, her thoughts were not very cheerful.

Six months ago, when her father had told the family that they were moving to a ranch out West, Jane had been glad. And at first she had loved their new home. Every day was bright and sunny, with plenty of time to play and to learn about ranch life.

But lately the family had had nothing but misfortunes. Some of the cattle had taken sick and died, and the hot desert winds had ruined the garden.

Now Mr. Wallace was away, trying to get more cattle. Jane felt sure he would not be back for Christmas. And her mother was too discouraged and too busy taking care of the ranch to make any Christmas plans.

"It doesn't seem right for Tim and Ann not to have a Christmas this year," Jane said to herself. "I've had plenty of good Christmases. But the twins are too little to remember our holiday fun back East. If they're to celebrate Christmas this year, I guess I'll have to be Santa Claus."

Jane leaned on her broom, thinking hard.

"The main thing," she decided, "is to get a Christmas tree. But where can I find a real one? Nothing but cactus and mesquite grows around here."

As Jane went about her duties, she kept wondering how to provide a Christmas tree. Then suddenly she stopped wondering.

"Why, it can be just any kind of a tree," she thought. "It can even be a mesquite bush. Only it has to look pretty. It has to *look* like a Christmas tree, with lots of pretty trimmings."

Jane hurried into the kitchen. "Mother!" she cried. "Where is our box of Christmas-tree ornaments?"

"I'm sorry, dear," replied Mrs. Wallace. "Those ornaments were all broken when our things got here. I must have packed them carelessly."

Jane sighed bitterly.

"Were you thinking of having a Christmas tree?" asked Mrs. Wallace, noting Jane's disappointment.

"Yes, Mother," Jane replied. "The twins are old enough now to remember Christmas. They should have a tree and gifts."

"You're right, Jane," said Mrs. Wallace. "But where can we get a tree? How can we provide gifts?"

Just then the twins rushed in. "Lunch!" they cried hungrily.

"We'll have it ready in a few moments," said their mother. "We'll have scrambled eggs and ham if you'll bring in some eggs."

As the twins dashed out to the henhouse, the wrinkles in Mrs. Wallace's forehead deepened in thought.

"My granny used to *make* pretties for her family's tree," she told Jane. "But I——"

Then Mrs. Wallace laughed. "Eggs!" she exclaimed. "Granny made ornaments from eggshells!"

Quickly Mrs. Wallace explained to Jane how this was done.

After lunch, while the two youngsters were taking their naps, Jane set to work with a dozen eggs. She poked a darning needle into the ends of each egg. After making holes a quarter of an inch wide, she held the egg over a bowl. Then she blew very gently into one end of the egg. The insides ran out the other end into the bowl, leaving an empty eggshell.

Jane dyed the shells with some Easter-egg dye that Mrs. Wallace found. "They'll make lovely ornaments," Jane said to her mother with satisfaction. "Your granny was very clever."

The girl's plans for Christmas grew and grew. She made lots of fancy cookies, some to eat and some to hang on the tree. One she cut like a big star. That was to go at the very top of the tree.

All the next day Jane kept trying to think of presents for the twins. Then Tim ran in with a round blue stone he had found.

"It's like a ball," he said. "I wish it would bounce like the one I lost."

"A ball," Jane repeated to herself. "Why, I'll *make* Timmy a ball."

She found yarn in her mother's scrap bag and wound it tightly into a ball. Then she covered the yarn with bright-colored scraps of cloth.

"It won't bounce like the rubber ball Tim lost," she thought. "But it's mighty pretty."

The yarn gave Jane another idea. "I'll make a stocking doll for Ann," she decided.

Finally it was the night before Christmas. The twins were in bed, and Mrs. Wallace was making a special Christmas pudding. Now it was time for Jane to find a tree and trim it. She stepped outside the house. Then she gave a little cry of delight.

The shining moon made the night almost as light as day. The desert sand looked snowy white, with dark pools where the cactus and mesquite cast their shadows.

"Why, the desert is beautiful!" the girl murmured. "It's as beautiful as our white Christmases back home."

But she must not linger. Running to the barn, Jane got a short-handled ax. Nearby she found just the mesquite tree she wanted. It was small enough for her to chop down with a few blows of the ax.

Jane carried the tree into the house and fixed it securely in a box filled with sand. Then she covered the box with pillowcases and scattered soap flakes over them to look like snow. With a darning needle, she ran strings through the cookies and the dyed egg-shells and then tied them to the branches.

Just as Jane finished, her mother came in. Mrs. Wallace gazed at the tree in amazement.

"Was your grandmother's tree any prettier than this?" Jane asked.

"No, dear," said her mother gently. "I'm sure no tree could be prettier than yours."

The next morning the twins' delight repaid Jane for all her work. The youngsters were enchanted with the tree and with their gifts.

Later, as they were all starting to eat their Christmas dinner, there was a sound at the door. Tim ran to open it.

"It's Daddy!" he shouted happily.

"Well!" said Mr. Wallace when he saw the tree. "I hurried back home to bring your Christmas, but apparently it's already here."

"It's Jane's idea," said her mother. "She thought the twins should have a tree. It's the first one they can remember."

"Look in my bag, Jane," said her father, smiling tenderly. "You will find some other things to help them remember Christmas."

Mr. Wallace had brought gifts for all his family, and they were so excited they could hardly eat their dinner.

That night when Jane helped her mother tuck the twins into bed, she smiled happily.

"They won't forget this first Christmas in the desert," she said. "None of us will."

Adventure in the Swamps

Johnny was a farm boy who lived near the Santee River swamps. One morning after breakfast he was sitting on the front steps, idly roping a gatepost. He pretended that the post was an alligator he was attempting to capture.

Ever since Johnny's big brother Henry had caught and tamed an alligator, Johnny had wanted one, too. Today he intended to get it.

He coiled the rope and tossed it over one shoulder. Then he went slowly out the gate, singing loudly.

Johnny sang so loudly, in fact, that his mother did not notice he had left the porch. The boy headed for the Santee River. He was thinking only about his alligator.

"I hope my 'gator won't be hiding in his cave under the riverbank," Johnny said to himself. "If he is, I'll just have to wait till he comes out."

As Johnny walked along, he remembered all the exciting things Henry had told him about alligators. At the same time, however, he began to feel a little guilty. His mother had told him it was dangerous for him to go alone into the swamps. But he had been so eager to catch an alligator that until now he had forgotten her warning.

"There's nothing to be afraid of in the swamps," Johnny argued aloud with himself. "And if Henry can catch a 'gator, I guess I can, too. Besides, I'm almost there. It would be a shame to turn back now."

The sound of his own voice encouraged the boy. He began to whistle. Before long he reached the swamp, still carrying the coiled rope over his shoulder.

Johnny walked along under cypress trees dripping with moss. He smelled the blossoms of the tupelo trees, where bees were busily gathering honey. His glance darted around eagerly. He wanted to catch all the sights of the Santee swamp.

He saw a turtle sunning itself on a big cypress log and tossed a stick at it. Then he came to a clump of leafy bushes heavy with ripe, juicy berries. On any other day he would have stopped to eat his fill. But today he was after his 'gator.

Johnny stopped just long enough to grab
a handful of the tasty berries. Then the
boy saw bees buzzing about a hollow tupelo
tree. He wondered if that was where they
had stored their honey. He would come back
later and find out, for no honey is sweeter
than tupelo honey from the swamps.

"Ah, coon tracks!" he said as he spied tiny
footprints. "I'll come again next winter and
try to catch him. If he's a big coon, I'll
trade him to Henry for his fiddle. Henry
wants a coon hide." Then Johnny forgot
about the coon. He had seen his 'gator!

It was a river alligator, about six feet in length. Johnny felt sure that he would be able to handle it. The alligator was sliding through the broom grass toward the river. Johnny was lucky. He had not expected to find his 'gator out of water.

Then the alligator saw Johnny. It lay dead still. Johnny noticed that it looked like an old cypress log.

The boy crept toward it cautiously, getting his rope ready to throw. But the alligator saw Johnny coming. It slid off toward the riverbank again.

Johnny coiled his rope and threw it at the animal. The rope caught on a tupelo tree. While the boy was getting it untangled, the alligator slid forward several yards nearer the river.

Again Johnny tried, and again he missed. He started to try a third time.

Suddenly he heard a warning rattle from behind a cypress log. Turning around, he saw eight feet of coiled rattlesnake and a broad, wicked-looking head. Johnny did not linger. He got away fast.

He did not stop to kill the snake, for he knew his 'gator was heading for the water. It had only a few yards to go. Once again Johnny threw his rope. It landed squarely about the alligator's thick neck, like a collar. Johnny felt very proud. Now he could pull his prize home. He would show Henry!

The alligator struggled fiercely against the rope. It flopped about, trying to get loose. Johnny grasped the rope more tightly. He pulled hard as the alligator squirmed to free itself from the rope.

Suddenly the alligator hooked its big tail around a cypress tree. Johnny could not budge the animal. It just lay and stared at Johnny with unblinking, snakelike eyes.

Henry had said that if a 'gator makes up his mind he won't budge, he just won't. So Johnny calmly sat down to wait until the alligator would unhook.

Johnny still grasped the rope tightly. He was keeping well out of reach of that tail. He knew that an alligator defends itself by slapping with its tail. And its slap is no gentle pat.

Finally the alligator unhooked its big tail. As Johnny started pulling again, he did not see something move in the nearby bushes.

Then the bushes parted, and a fierce wild pig appeared. Her wicked eyes flashed, and she was grunting furiously.

Panic seized Johnny as the pig opened her ugly mouth. He looked about frantically for a tree. But none was near enough to climb before the beast could reach him. Tightening his grasp on the rope, he moved farther away from the pig. How he wished that he had paid attention to his mother's warning!

Suddenly the angry pig lunged at Johnny. The alligator was now between him and the pig, but apparently the pig had not noticed it. The alligator gave a quick flip of its tail, and the pig tumbled over.

As the pig got up and tore madly into the swamp, Johnny laughed out loud. He felt much better. He was thankful to be alive.

Coiling his rope as he went, he walked toward the alligator's head. He knew that the alligator's tail could not reach him if he kept in front of the beast.

Finally Johnny got up close to the animal and rubbed his hand over the tough, leathery head. Henry had said, "A 'gator likes to be petted."

The animal's jaws fell open, and its snake-like eyes closed sleepily. Johnny slipped the rope off the thick neck.

"I've changed my mind," he said. "You're my 'gator all right. But you saved my life, so I'll repay you by leaving you here. You'd miss this old Santee swamp."

Then Johnny started for home, singing. The alligator slid off through the grass.

Judy's Chickens

Judy Woods stood by the door of her very own chicken house. Carefully she counted her chickens as they ate their breakfast.

"Eighty-two, eighty-three—but where is the eighty-fourth?" Judy peered anxiously into the dimness of the chicken house.

She was convinced that her chickens were the finest in the whole world. She had fed and watered them ever since they were pale-yellow fluffy balls only two days old. Now they were three months old and ready to be sold. Judy's father was taking them to the market in Clayborn tomorrow.

"Oh, dear," sighed Judy. "I hope nothing has happened to one of my chickens."

Just then the eighty-fourth chicken ran out from behind the chicken house.

"Judy! It's time for school," cried Mrs. Woods from the back porch.

Judy shut the chicken-house door and ran to get her bicycle. It would not do to be late for school this Thursday. Her teacher was to give the class directions for their Easter trip to the St. Louis zoo on Saturday.

Hopping on her bike, Judy waved good-by to her mother and rode swiftly off.

Soon Judy came to the tiny farm where her good friend Mrs. Pepper lived all alone. Mrs. Pepper was feeding her chickens.

"Good morning!" Judy called gaily.

"Hello!" Mrs. Pepper called back. "I'm going to Clayborn this afternoon. Maybe I can get a summer job in the factory there."

"Well, good luck!" Judy shouted as she sped on down the road.

Before long she came to the Banks farm, which was a chicken farm like most of the others in that region. Mary Banks and her brother Bob were coming down the walk on their bicycles.

"Say, Judy," said Bob, "did you hear the radio broadcast this morning? There was a tornado just two miles away last night."

"I hope we never have one here," Mary said with a shiver.

"Me, too," said Judy. "It might kill my chickens. I'm counting on the money that Dad gets for them to pay for my St. Louis trip."

"You and your old chickens," laughed Bob. "You'd think they were made of gold. And wouldn't one of your chickens look funny with all the feathers blown off it!"

"Oh, don't mind him, Judy," said Mary. "He's always teasing me, too."

The children hurried on to the little white schoolhouse. When all the pupils were in their seats, the teacher told them the final plans for the St. Louis trip. Judy felt as though she could hardly wait. She had been looking forward to this wonderful trip ever since it had first been mentioned.

Four o'clock came at last. Judy dashed out to her bicycle. She was so eager to see if her chickens were all right that she did not even wait for Mary.

Without warning, something cold hit her on the nose as she rode along. Then something bounced off her forehead. Tiny hailstones were falling from dark, puffy clouds. More hailstones hit her face—bigger ones.

"My poor chickens!" she gasped. "They're outside! I closed the chicken-house door, and they can't get in."

She passed the Banks farm. Mr. and Mrs. Banks were running about, closing up their chicken houses.

Judy looked at the sky. A huge cloud in the west looked ugly and purple. It curved and moved around like boiling syrup.

Now Judy was passing Mrs. Pepper's tiny farm. The chickens were pressing against their house. Their door was closed, too.

"Why doesn't Mrs. Pepper let them in?" the girl wondered. Then she remembered. Mrs. Pepper had gone to Clayborn.

As Judy rode on, the hail ceased. There was a queer yellow light everywhere, and a peculiar quiet. Judy looked at the western sky again. The huge cloud was closer now, and it had something long like an elephant's trunk hanging from it.

Judy stared at the cloud in panic. "That really must be a tornado cloud," she thought. "My chickens will all be killed!"

Her father and mother would not know that she had closed her chicken-house door. And they would not notice it because the chicken house was almost hidden behind the barn.

Judy sped on, her heart pounding. How could she go to St. Louis if all her chickens were killed? Then she thought of her good friend Mrs. Pepper. *Her* chicken money paid for most of her living. What would she do if her chickens were blown away?

It was a difficult choice for Judy to make, but she did not hesitate long. She turned around and rode back to the tiny farm. If she never went to St. Louis, she could not let Mrs. Pepper lose her precious chickens.

Judy opened the chicken-house door, and the clucking chickens scurried inside.

Then a blinding rain began to fall, and the wind blew fiercely. It was too late for Judy to go home now. She hurried inside with the chickens and shut the door tight.

Judy watched the storm anxiously. The wind was slashing at the trees, breaking off branches and whipping them through the air.

"Oh, my poor chickens!" Judy cried again.

Suddenly all was quiet, and the sun came out. Judy opened the door cautiously. To the west the sky was blue. To the east the dark clouds were hurrying away.

Once more the girl mounted her bicycle. The muddy road made the going hard. Here and there tree limbs lay on the road. Then she had to get off and push her bicycle around them. But finally she reached home.

"Judy!" her mother cried, hurrying out of the house. "Where have you been?"

Judy headed for her chicken house.

"I'll tell you later, Mother," she called back. "I have to see if my chickens are all right. I left the door of their house shut. They couldn't get in out of the tornado!"

"Wait, Judy!" cried her mother. "Your chickens are safe. The tornado didn't hurt anything around here. It passed through the woods."

The girl was so happy that she whirled her mother around in a little dance.

"Stop, Judy," laughed Mrs. Woods. "Tell me—where were you during the storm?"

Judy giggled. "I was in Mrs. Pepper's chicken house with the chickens," she said. "I stopped there to let her chickens into their house. The wind must have blown the door shut while she was gone. I was afraid the tornado would carry them away."

Mrs. Woods looked at her daughter with pride. "Mrs. Pepper will be thankful she has such a good friend," she said. "Now come inside and try on your Easter dress."

"It will be my St. Louis zoo dress, too," said Judy, skipping gaily up the steps.

Maple-Sugar Time

"Why did Mother and Dad have to choose Vermont to move to?" Robert Huff grumbled to himself. "There's nothing to do here but skate, skate, skate! At home we might be playing baseball by this time."

It was the first Saturday in March. The Huff family had left New York City for their new home in Vermont only two weeks ago. Now Robert was going with Jason Peters and Ben Dickson to the skating pond.

"See the crows!" cried Jason as some big black birds flapped over the bare trees.

"That means spring," said Ben. "The sap will be running soon if it warms up a bit."

"What's so wonderful about sap?" Robert asked. "All I hear in this old town is maple trees and sap, maple syrup, maple sugar."

Ben and Jason stared at Robert. After a moment Jason said, "If that's the way you feel about our town, we won't bother you."

The two boys ran toward the pond and left Robert standing alone in the path. Angrily he walked back to town.

During the weekend the sun shone warmly in the daytime, but the nights were cold. It was good sap-running weather.

When Robert arrived at school on Monday morning, not even the teacher was there.

"It must be a special Vermont holiday," Robert decided.

Just then a sled load of laughing boys and girls came along the road. "Come and help us scatter buckets at Peters' Woods," a girl called. "No school till the sap-run is over."

"I'm too busy," Robert replied, although he really had nothing to do.

But as the sled went by with its load of shining buckets and cheerful boys and girls, Robert suddenly felt lonesome.

On his way home Robert passed Peters'
Woods. When he saw all the people working there, he stopped to watch. Mr. Peters
was boring a hole in the south side of a tree,
where most of the branches grew. After the
hole was bored and blown free of sawdust,
his grandson Jason fitted a steel spout into
it, hammering the spout in firmly.

Then Ben Dickson hooked a bucket on the
spout. Over the bucket he put a cover that
was shaped like a tiny roof. "To keep the
snow and dirt out," Robert guessed.

Mr. Peters and the two boys went on to
the next tree. Nearby other teams of three
were boring holes, fitting spouts, and hanging buckets.

Robert thought the work looked like fun. But he was too stubborn to offer Jason and Ben his help. He walked on down the road.

Soon he came to a little shack. It was a sap house, or sugar house, where the sap was boiled into syrup.

A sled stood before the shack. On the sled was a tank with a pipe leading down to another tank where the sap was stored until it could be boiled into syrup. The driver was letting the sap pour down the pipe.

"Hello, Robert," called the man. "Have you come to see how we make syrup?"

Robert recognized Mr. Swift, who worked in the bank. "Why, hello, Mr. Swift," the boy said. "Is the bank closed?"

"Everything's closed for the sap-running," replied Mr. Swift. "We have to gather and boil the sap into syrup in a few days. This sap weather usually doesn't last long."

He closed the tap on the pipe and started to drive the tank back for more sap.

"Maybe I can help you," offered Robert.

"Sure, hop on," said Mr. Swift. "You can empty buckets into this tank. It takes forty gallons of sap to make one gallon of syrup. That's a lot of emptying."

Mr. Swift chuckled. "I was the first one in town to have my buckets scattered. I'll start my boiling tonight."

After helping Mr. Swift all day, Robert ached with weariness. He felt as though he had emptied thousands of gallons of sap. But after eating dinner, he felt fine.

"Dad!" he cried. "Why don't we go down to watch Mr. Swift boil his sap?"

"I'd like to, Son. But I must write some important letters. You go ahead, though."

Robert put on his warmest sweater and jacket and went down to the sugar house. Its windows were glowing brightly.

Mr. Swift was not in the sugar house. But Robert saw a long pan on top of a narrow wood stove. Under a cloud of steam, gallons of maple sap boiled in the pan.

While Robert watched, he began to notice that the sap was boiling more slowly than it had at first. "The fire must be getting low," he thought. "I wonder if I shouldn't add some wood."

Robert watched a little longer. Only a few bubbles broke the surface of the sap. Quickly the boy threw some wood into the stove. The sap started to bubble violently.

"What if it boils over?" Robert worried as the bubbles rose higher and higher.

The boiling sap was almost even with the top of the pan. Robert knew that he would have to do something. He jerked open the stove door and tried to pull out some of the wood. Immediately the flames leaped out at him. He banged the door shut with his foot.

Now the syrup was beginning to boil over. "Maybe I should take out some sap," he thought. As he looked frantically around the shack, he noticed a pitcher containing a little cream. Robert grabbed the pitcher. Dipping it quickly into the pan, cream and all, he lifted out a pitcherful of sap.

The bubbling sap quieted down at once and fell an inch or two in the pan.

"How mysterious!" Robert thought. "I didn't take out *that* much sap. Maybe Mr. Swift can explain the mystery."

Robert ran to the door and looked down the snowy path. It was empty.

Suddenly he heard a cry, "Help! Help!" Guided by the voice, Robert raced into the woods. There he found Mr. Swift limping painfully along.

"I've hurt my leg," he moaned. "I must get back to the shack. I'm afraid the syrup is ruined by this time."

"Here," said Robert, "lean on me. Don't worry about the syrup. It's all right now. I built up the fire to keep the syrup boiling. Then it began to boil over, so I used your pitcher. It worked like magic."

"Now tell me something," said Mr. Swift as he limped to the shack. "How did a city boy like you know that mixing a little cream in the sap would keep it from boiling over?"

"Cream!" cried Robert. "Why, I *didn't* know. So that's what did the trick!"

The next day everyone in the Vermont town knew how Robert had saved the syrup. On his arrival at the shack to help Mr. Swift, he found Jason and Ben already there.

"We came to help, too," said Jason. He added gruffly, "You didn't do so badly last night—for a city boy."

"Would you like to come to our sugaring-off party Thursday?" Ben asked. "That's when we make maple-sugar candy for everyone who helped during the sap-run."

"I certainly would like to come," Robert replied. "I want to taste this fine maple sugar that my home town makes."

"Have some right now," offered Mr. Swift. "I boiled down a small panful of syrup into sugar last night after you'd gone. I thought you might like to try some!"

The Quiet Mountains

"Oo-oooo-ooh!" screamed a train whistle.

"That will be Number Nine coming in," Sarah thought as she stood looking out her window at Mount Stephen. "Father will be home to breakfast soon."

All day long and all night, too, the sound of engines could be heard in Field, a small railroad town in Canada. The town lay in a deep valley, with the Rocky Mountains rising steeply on both sides.

Along the bottom of this narrow valley ran the Kicking Horse River, the highway, and the railway.

From "Train Whistles in the Mountains" in *Across Canada* by Clare Bice. Copyright, 1949, by The Macmillan Company. Adapted by permission of the publishers.

Sarah gave a last look at the snow-capped mountain and went downstairs to breakfast. Her father was just coming in from the railroad yards. "Numbers Fifteen and Sixteen will be taken off next week," he announced. "The vacation season is just about over."

"I wish people would really stop off here at Field," Sarah said. "They just stay a few minutes while the pushers are hooked on."

The extra engines were called "pushers," though they really helped *pull* the trains up the mountains. It took two and frequently three of the pushers to haul a train up the mountain pass and through the tunnels.

"Oh, by the way, Sarah," said her father. "Your friend Molly wants to see you. I saw her when I came from the roundhouse."

Later that forenoon, as Sarah was going to the grocery store, she met Molly.

"Guess what!" Molly cried. "A man has rented our front bedroom. His name is Mr. Brooks, and he paints pictures. He's going up the valley this afternoon to paint. So I asked if you and I could go along."

"What did he say?" asked Sarah eagerly.

"He said that he'd be pleased to have our company," Molly answered.

"Oh, good!" said Sarah. "Perhaps he'll paint Mount Stephen. There's a fine view way up the highway."

After lunch the three of them crossed the bridge over the river at Field and walked for a while along the road that wound up the left side of the valley. Looking back across the valley, they saw Mount Stephen rising ten thousand feet into the sky. At the base of the mountain snuggled the town of Field.

"See how the train curves around the sides of Stephen," Molly pointed out to Mr. Brooks.

Just then a truck drove up behind them.
"It's our neighbor, Mr. White!" exclaimed
Sarah. "If he'll give us a lift, we can go
much higher. Then we'll get a better view
of the top of Mount Stephen."

Mr. White drove the girls and Mr. Brooks
on up the curving slope. After a while they
crossed a bridge back to the right side of
the valley. When they came to a level spot,
Sarah cried, "This is the view I meant!"

Mr. White let his three passengers out.
After promising to pick them up on his
way back, he drove on up the sloping road.

"Look! Isn't that nice?" said Sarah.

"It certainly is!" cried Mr. Brooks. "It
will be a lovely, peaceful view to paint."

He started unpacking his paints at once. Sarah thought that perhaps she and Molly should leave Mr. Brooks in quiet to paint his picture. So she said, "Molly, there's a fine fossil bed a little farther up the road. We might look for some interesting fossils while Mr. Brooks paints."

"I'm going to stay and watch," Molly said.

Sarah would have preferred to stay, too. But now that she had mentioned the fossil bed, she decided to go there by herself.

She walked up the curving mountain road, feeling a bit lonely and uneasy. Near Field she did not mind walking alone, but she was not so familiar with this part of the valley. What if she should meet a grizzly! She was not afraid of black bears, but she had a deep fear of grizzlies.

She felt better when she came to a spot where the railway track crossed the road— she was used to railroads. And nearby were two houses where the track workers lived.

The fossil bed could not be far off now. Sarah kept on walking, though now and then little noises in the woods made her jump.

Then Sarah saw a bear in the bushes by the road! The girl's heart skipped a beat, and she stopped still. But it was a black bear, not a grizzly. Followed by two cubs, the bear came out onto the highway. After staring at Sarah for a moment, she hustled her cubs into the woods.

Shivering, Sarah hurried on to the fossil bed. There she saw some pebbles that were like curious little animals. People said that long, long ago they had really been animals. But they had been buried in the mud for so long that they had turned to stone.

Sarah picked up half a dozen fossils and put them in her sweater pocket. Suddenly she heard a rumble farther up the road.

The rumble grew louder and louder. Now she could see something about a quarter of a mile ahead. A landslide was starting down the steep slope above the railroad track.

As Sarah watched, a piece of the mountain seemed to fall away. It went crashing and rumbling down, carrying with it huge rocks and trees. Finally it landed right across the railroad track!

The earth and rocks continued to slide for several minutes. Sarah stood glued to the ground. Then she remembered that Molly's father would be bringing his pusher engine down this track soon!

Sarah turned and ran back down the road as fast as her legs could carry her. One of the track workers' houses at the crossing would surely have a telephone. If she could call the station at Field, she thought, then Molly's father would be warned that the track was buried under a slide.

She pounded frantically on the door of the first house. No answer. She pushed open the door and rushed in. No one was there. But on the wall was a telephone!

"Hello! Hello!" Sarah shouted loudly into the mouthpiece. "Is this Field? I'm at the highway crossing. . . . Yes, that's right. . . . There's a landslide across the track about a quarter of a mile up beyond the fossil bed. . . . You know already? . . . Oh, I forgot that the signal wire would warn you. . . . That's fine. . . . Good-by."

Slowly Sarah hung up the receiver. She leaned against the wall, trying to steady her shaking knees and trembling lips. The man at Field had said that the trains would be stopped before they got to the buried track. There would be no wreck.

When Sarah joined Mr. Brooks and Molly, they were looking at his completed painting. Molly was pointing at it and saying something to Mr. Brooks. Apparently they had not heard the noise of the landslide.

"Hello," Mr. Brooks greeted Sarah. "Did you get some good fossils? I hope Mr. White comes back soon to pick us up. I thought I heard thunder a while ago."

But Sarah could think of nothing except the picture. She gazed at it eagerly.

"I'm afraid my painting isn't very good," said Mr. Brooks, frowning.

"Oh, it *is* good!" Sarah exclaimed. "It's— it's perfect, I think."

"No," insisted Mr. Brooks, "it isn't what I wanted to paint. It doesn't show the silence and peace of these mountains."

Silence? Peace? Sarah smiled to herself. The mountains might look quiet and peaceful to Mr. Brooks. But he had not met a bear or seen a dangerous landslide. How amazed he would be when he learned of the exciting things that had just happened to her on these mountains!

Alarm in the Night

After a warm, sunny day the Southern California night was sharp with sudden cold. Now the moon was turning the leaves in the Pages' orange grove to bright silver.

In her room thirteen-year-old Susan Page switched on the bedside radio. If she kept the radio turned low, she could listen to her favorite program, "California Pinto."

As the story went on, Susan listened with growing delight. "How wonderful it would be to own a pony!" she thought. Suddenly the radio program was interrupted.

"ATTENTION, FRUIT GROWERS!" came the radio announcer's voice. "The temperature in Southern California may drop to freezing before morning. Light your orchard heaters to save your crops!"

Susan drew a frightened breath. Suppose their oranges should freeze! For a moment she thought of waking her mother and her younger brother Joey. But her mother had been up very early that morning helping Dad pick oranges. She needed her night's rest. And Joey would know less about saving the rest of the crop than Susan herself did.

"Oh, dear," the girl sighed. "If only Dad were here!"

That afternoon Mr. Page had gone to take part of his orange crop to market in town. He would not come back until tomorrow. Susan had often helped in the orange groves, but she had never lighted the heaters.

"Maybe the temperature won't drop after all," she thought. "This California weather changes quickly in the orange belt. And if the temperature does fall dangerously low, our own frost-alarm bell will ring."

With this comforting thought, Susan was soon fast asleep. In her dreams she was riding a swift pinto.

All at once she awakened with a start. A bell was ringing loudly. "The frost alarm!" she cried. "The temperature did drop."

Susan heard running footsteps in the hall followed by a knock on her door.

"Mother says to get up!" shouted Joey. "Our oranges will freeze!"

After Susan had pulled on her sweater and blue jeans, Mrs. Page came by. "We'll have to light the orchard heaters," she told the children. "I know they are kept filled with oil, but I've never lit them."

"I know how," Susan said encouragingly. "I've watched Dad do it. He lit them with a can with a long spout. Dad called the can a torch. He filled the can with oil. Then he lit the end of the spout and touched the flame to the heater."

"Joey is a little young for that kind of work," Mrs. Page said doubtfully. "But I need all the help I can get. He'll just have to be extra careful."

They all started immediately to the shed near the grove. Here the torches were kept. Susan helped her mother fill them with oil.

"When we light the heaters," Susan told Joey, "warm smoke comes out the pipe in each heater and floats up under the trees. That warms the air and keeps the oranges from freezing."

With torches in hand, the three of them hastened toward the trees. Mrs. Page lit the wick of each torch. Quickly they began to light the iron heaters.

As they went farther in among the trees, the warm, gassy smoke drifting up from the oil heaters made it a little hard to breathe. Mrs. Page heard a choking sound.

"Joey!" she called. "Are you all right?"

"My throat and eyes burn," Joey replied.

"Go back to the house, then," ordered his mother.

"No," said the boy bravely. "I want to help."

Finally the last heater was lit. The whole grove was now protected by a light cloud of warm, smoky air.

With relief Mrs. Page put out the flames of the torches. Then she and the children left the orange grove and threw themselves down on the ground to rest. The cold air chilled them now, but they were too weary to get up.

"Your throat and eyes will be all right," Mrs. Page comforted Joey. "But that was a hard night's work. I don't know what I would have done without your help, children. I never could have lit all those heaters in time to save the oranges."

At last Mrs. Page said, "We'd better go back to the house." And through the dim light of early morning they stumbled home.

Shortly afterwards the rumble of a truck was heard outside. Then the door opened.

"Anyone home?" boomed Mr. Page's voice. "I saw smoke in the grove as I approached the house. There must be a fine ranch hand around here."

Mr. Page turned to his wife. "Did you manage all those heaters by yourself?"

"The children did just as much as I did," said Mrs. Page. "They were a great help."

"Well, I'm proud of all of you," said Mr. Page. "I heard the frost warning over the radio. I started to hurry home, but my truck broke down on a mountain detour. I was sure we'd lose our fruit."

Then he smiled. "Would you two like to go over to the corral of the Double-X ranch this morning?" he asked the children.

"The Double-X?" said Susan. "What for?"

"Every good ranch hand needs a horse," replied her father. "I know two fine ponies there that are just begging for a new home."

"You mean they're for us?" cried Joey.

"Of course," said Mr. Page. "Well, what are we waiting for?"

"Just to catch our breath!" replied Susan.

The School Train

In a one-room cabin deep in the northern forests a trapper named Antoine lived with his two motherless sons, Tony and John.

One snowy November night Antoine said, "Boys, it's time for me to set out my traplines or we won't have any furs to sell at the trading post. I may be gone for a month or two. I don't like to leave you, but we must have money for food and clothes."

"Don't worry, Papa," said red-haired Tony. "John and I can manage."

Antoine banked the fire in the stove, and the boys got into their wooden bunks. Soon they were fast asleep.

The next morning Antoine said, "I've told Ace Stone that I'm leaving today. So if you need help, go to him."

The boys nodded. They had always liked the fisherman who lived five miles away.

Shortly after the trapper had gone, Ace pounded on the door of the cabin.

"I've thought of something you might like to do while your father is away," he said.

"What is it?" asked both boys at once.

"Well," Ace began, "there's a supply train that goes to the lumber camps. One of the cars is a schoolroom for boys and girls who live in the forest. There are books, desks, and a teacher!"

"John and I have never been to a school," Tony burst out. "How I wish we could learn to read and write!"

Ace smiled. "The train leaves the school car in a camp while it is delivering supplies farther on," he continued. "Then it returns later to take the school car to another camp. The car is at Pine Camp now, twenty miles away. I can't take you to it this time, but when it returns to Pine Camp, I will."

"When do you suppose the school car will come back to Pine Camp?" asked John.

"I'm not sure," replied Ace. "But it will be soon. Maybe two or three weeks. Then we'll go."

After Ace had left, Tony and John talked over the news. "Let's not wait for Ace to take us to the school car," suggested Tony. "Let's go by ourselves tomorrow."

Early the next morning they collected the things necessary for their trip. Besides a tent, they packed sleeping bags, cans of milk and vegetables, a saucepan for cooking, and some extra clothes.

Just as the boys were ready to go, Tony thought of something. "Suppose Papa comes home before we get back from the school," he said. "Or suppose Ace comes by and we are not here. They would worry."

"We must leave a message," John said.

"How?" inquired Tony. "We can't write. And neither Papa nor Ace can read."

"Watch!" said John. Taking a small piece of blackened wood from the stove, he began to draw on the clean table top.

Quickly John finished the picture-message. He had drawn a train and the figures of two boys heading toward it.

"That will tell Papa and Ace where we've gone," he said.

Both boys knew the forest and the trail to Pine Camp. But traveling was difficult, especially in the deep forest. For three long days the boys walked steadily. They camped out each night and built fires to heat their food. At dusk on the third day they arrived at the camp. There they met a man.

"Hello," he said. "Where are you from?"

"From our cabin twenty miles away," Tony said. "We've come to see the school car."

"Fine!" said the man. "I'm Mr. Chalmers, the teacher. Come, I'll show you the car. Mrs. Chalmers and I live in the car with our daughter Mary."

The school car was on a nearby railroad siding. As they all walked toward it, the boys told the teacher their names and how they happened to be there.

To the boys' surprise the car contained three rooms. The first was a tiny kitchen. Next was a larger room with some chairs, day beds, and a table. There Mr. Chalmers introduced the boys to his wife and daughter. They welcomed Tony and John warmly.

Then the boys saw the schoolroom. There were blackboards, two rows of desks, maps of the world, and cases of books.

"May we camp by the car and go to school while Papa is trapping?" asked Tony.

"Yes, indeed," replied the teacher. "We shall be glad to have you in the class."

That night Tony and John ate supper with the teacher's family. "Tonight," said Mr. Chalmers, "you'd better sleep in the school-room. It's too late to put up your tent."

Early the next morning the boys set up their tent and cooked breakfast over a fire. When the school bell rang, they hurried into the car with the children from the lumber camp. In all, there were thirteen pupils, six of whom were Indians.

"Good morning," said the teacher. Then he told the pupils about Tony and John and their twenty-mile walk to join the school.

"Now," said Mr. Chalmers, "we will stand and sing the song of Canada."

Tony and John stumbled over the words, but they enjoyed singing with the others.

After the song came reading and writing lessons. Then Mr. Chalmers read a story. Tony liked the story very much. He decided that even though learning printed words was hard, he wanted to be able to read stories for himself as soon as possible.

During the lunch hour the other children gathered around Tony and John. "Tell us again about your trip through the forest," they demanded eagerly. Soon the children were all talking together like old friends.

The next two weeks sped quickly by. Then it was time for the supply train to pick up the school car and take it farther into the wilderness.

"The car will not be back for two weeks," Mr. Chalmers explained to the pupils. "So you must work at home those two weeks."

That night Tony asked his brother, "Shall we go back home while the car is gone?"

"Let's talk to Mrs. Chalmers," John said.

A little later they did. "I have a plan," said Tony shyly. "I thought we could travel with the school car to the next camp. Then we could keep on going to school."

"That's a fine plan, boys," Mrs. Chalmers told them. "I'm sure your father would like you to get all the schooling you can."

When the school car left the camp Friday, Tony and John were on it. The boys were thrilled to be riding on a train. And they were looking forward to going to school with the children of the new lumber camp.

Two weeks later the car was returned to Pine Camp. Monday morning the pupils all met in the school car. Tony and John were delighted to see their old friends again.

As the singing started, the boys noticed the arrival of two men at the door. It was Ace Stone and their father!

"Papa!" cried the boys, rushing to greet Antoine.

"The boys' father returned home two days ago," Ace explained to Mr. Chalmers. "He found a picture-message in his cabin. So that's how we knew where the boys were."

"We are very proud of these boys," said Mr. Chalmers. Quickly he picked up a small book and handed it to Tony. "Here, show your father how you can read," he said.

Taking the thin book, Tony read it easily from cover to cover. Then Mr. Chalmers gave it to John, who also read it through.

Antoine beamed at his sons. "I—I cannot say how I feel," he stammered. His voice was choked with happiness.

Mr. Chalmers praised the boys' fine work at school. "I hope they will keep coming," he said.

"I will see that they do," promised their father seriously.

"Oh, good!" cried John. "Then Tony and I can learn to read much thicker books!"

A Camp in the Canyon

The moment the Howard family laid eyes
on the clearing in the canyon, they decided
that it was a perfect place to camp. Thick
pine forests grew on either side, and beyond
them rose the high canyon walls.

While Mr. Howard chopped wood for a
fire, Mrs. Howard started supper. Jill went
to a nearby spring for a pail of water, and
Tom built a rock stove not far from the tent.

As Tom was starting the fire, he heard a sharp voice call, "Say, there!"

A boy about Tom's own age had entered the clearing. Over his shoulder he carried a trout rod.

"Hello," said Tom in a friendly voice.

The boy pointed his trout rod at the fire. "Put that out," he said sternly. "You can't build fires here."

His tone made Tom a little angry. "Who are you?" he asked.

"I'm Louis Cook," replied the boy. "This is my dad's land. He won't permit campers."

Hearing the boys, Mr. Howard came over. "Hello," he said. "What's the trouble?"

"Dad won't permit campers on his land," Louis repeated. "Campers start forest fires."

"Well, we are always very careful about fires," said Mr. Howard, smiling. "We have built this rock stove in the open, and we never go off and leave a fire burning. If you tell your father that, maybe he'll permit us to camp here for a few days."

"Dad isn't home," answered the boy in the same unfriendly tone as before.

"All right," replied Mr. Howard. "We'll find another place for our camp."

As the boy walked away, Mr. Howard put out the fire. Then the family packed their things and left in search of another spot.

"There are plenty of good places to camp," said Mr. Howard. "We'll find one soon."

Fortunately they found one before dark on a ranch farther up the canyon. "We'll ask permission this time," said Mr. Howard as he drove to the ranch house.

To the family's relief, the rancher agreed to let them stay. "I think I can recognize good campers," he added. "You don't look like careless folks who would leave fires to destroy the forests."

The Howards promised that they would be careful. Soon they were settled in the new place. Tom and Jill did not like it so well as the first place, but at least they knew that they were welcome.

The moon was up before they had finished eating supper. The calmness of the summer night was broken only by the faint chirping of the crickets.

The next day all the family explored the canyon. It proved to be very exciting.

Tom discovered a deserted shack in which pack rats had hidden their stolen treasures. There were brass pins, a gold buckle, and other shiny objects. Nearby was a stream where Mr. Howard could cast for trout.

Small animals and brilliantly colored birds kept Jill busy with her camera. Once the family startled a dainty fawn. As the fawn leaped out of sight, bluejays scolded them noisily.

One morning Tom and Jill climbed up to
the fire tower of the ranger station. Dick
Sharp, the ranger on lookout duty, let them
look through his field glasses at the timber
region below. How close it looked! Then
he explained how field glasses and airplanes
helped the rangers patrol the forests.

"A fire patrol is always on duty," he said.
"We must watch for the first sign of a fire,
for it could ruin acres and acres of timber.
Electric storms and careless campers cause
us the most worry."

Jill looked out over the pine forests that seemed to meet the western sky.

"Don't you ever get lonesome?" she asked the ranger.

"We haven't time to get lonesome," Dick Sharp answered with a smile. "We're far too busy. Patrolling these forests is quite a job, even with the help of planes."

Jill and Tom thanked the ranger for his kindness and started home. As they left, he added, "I know you'll help us prevent fires. Remember, a single careless act may start a fire that could destroy all this fine timber."

Halfway down the canyon, Tom suddenly stopped. "I smell something burning!" he exclaimed.

They hurried along, looking on every side for a curl of smoke or a blaze. Finally they discovered a patch of burning moss.

"Get some water! Quick!" Tom said.

A few steps away was a brook. But they had nothing to hold water, not even a cap.

"Oh, look!" Jill cried in alarm as a patch of dry pine needles burst into flames.

"Let's try to stamp the fire out!" cried Tom. "Our boots are heavy."

The two were so busy at their task that they did not see Louis Cook running toward them with his trout rod. Not until a dry branch snapped beneath his feet did the two children look up.

"Hi!" Tom shouted. "Come and help us put this fire out."

Louis threw down his trout rod. "So you *did* start a fire!" he cried angrily.

"We didn't start it," Jill denied.

"Well," said Louis, "whether you did or not, we'll have to put it out." Pulling off his sweater, he soaked it in the brook and handed it to Jill. "Beat the flames with it," he said. "We boys can use our shirts."

Quickly both boys peeled off their woolen shirts. For a time all three fought the fire desperately.

"It's no use," Louis said, throwing down his shirt. "We can't stop it. I wish I had a shovel. I could dig a ditch around the fire. A lot of timber will be burned unless the patrol sees this fire soon."

"I'll go and get Dad," said Jill. "He'll know what to do."

"Good!" cried Louis. "Your brother and I will keep working. But hurry!"

"Tell Dad to bring a shovel," Tom called as Jill sped toward the camp.

Twenty minutes later Jill returned with her father. With them were Mr. Cook and other ranchers. By this time the rangers who patrolled the region had arrived on a truck with their fire-fighting tools. They were already fighting the fire.

Mr. Howard put Jill in the rangers' truck, which was parked at a safe distance.

Then he joined the men who were digging a ditch to prevent the fire from spreading. Two of the rangers were slashing away the brushwood that was catching fire from the flying sparks. Other rangers were beating the blazing grass with sacks that had been soaked in the brook. Tom and Louis were beating the grass, too, working together like old friends.

A stiff breeze fanned the fire toward the south. For three hours the men fought on. Their faces were scorched and blackened by the heat and smoke. Then it began to rain. The light sprinkle grew into a steady downpour. Soon the entire canyon was soaked.

"The timber's safe!" shouted a ranger, and the men ceased work in weary relief.

Mr. Cook took off his scorched gloves and shook hands with Mr. Howard. "Thanks for your help," he said. "If all campers were like your family, I'd put up signs saying *Welcome* instead of *Keep Out*. After this you may camp on my land any time."

The
Great Outdoors

A Zoo Without Bars

The full October moon splashed light and shadow over a wide, grassy meadow. In this shadowy light three children were advancing quietly across the meadow.

"Every wild thing that walks at night will be out under this moon," Jim, the older boy, said. "I'm going to give a talk in school Tuesday on the wild animals around here. We ought to see a lot of them tonight."

"Do you suppose we'll see a fox?" asked his sister June eagerly.

"Not if he sees us first," Jim said softly. "Remember, we must be very quiet."

Jim continued, "I found a rabbit run this morning. Let's go there and watch."

Soon the children were lying comfortably on a fallen tree that was screened by two bushes. David yawned loudly.

"Shhhh," June told her younger brother. "Don't make so much noise."

"Look carefully," Jim whispered. "You can see how the tall grass has been eaten away and pushed down to form open tunnels. This place is full of these rabbit trails."

Five minutes later June noticed something that made her stiffen. She grabbed Jim's hand and pointed.

"Skunk," Jim told her, and chuckled softly. "He isn't at all afraid of us. And he isn't as bad as most people think. He eats insects and small animals that are harmful to crops. I think he deserves the few eggs he gobbles up when he visits farms."

The neat black-and-white creature walked carelessly through the grass. Occasionally he paused to sniff and scratch in the earth. Then he settled down to do some serious digging.

"What's he found?" asked David.

The question was answered when a mouse jumped between the skunk's feet. But the tiny mouse was too slow to escape the sharp teeth that snapped on him.

"That skunk will eat a dozen more mice before morning," Jim remarked. "Maybe a few crickets, too."

Slowly the skunk walked on. He vanished from sight in the tall grass.

A moment later June caught her breath as a steady thump, thump, thump sounded from the meadow.

She drew closer to Jim. "What's that?" she whispered uneasily. "It sounds like a giant walking."

"It's a rabbit kicking the ground," replied Jim. "Something has alarmed him—maybe the skunk. He's sending a message to the other rabbits around here to watch out for possible danger. He isn't quite sure what's going on. So he drums on the ground with his hind legs to warn his friends."

"Oh," sighed June in relief. "I thought it must be something huge and dangerous."

There was a slight movement in a grass tunnel, and a rabbit hopped out. He began nibbling on a clump of clover. Soon he was joined by another rabbit, and another, and another.

June wiggled with delight. "Look!" she said softly. "It's a bunny party!"

Jim pressed her arm for silence.

"Just wait," he said with a low chuckle. "You really *will* see a party."

All at once the rabbits began leaping high
into the air. Then they bounded in circles.
Their powerful hind legs acted as springs
beneath them.

Gradually the rabbits formed one big circle
like a merry-go-round. Each animal seemed
to be trying to leap higher than the others.

Just how long this play might have lasted
none of the watchers knew. For suddenly a
shadow crossed the moon, and the meadow
was filled with thumps of alarm and fleeing
rabbits. The shadow took clearer shape. It
swooped close to the ground and then rose
again on strong wings.

"Don't be frightened," Jim whispered. "It was just an owl after a mouse."

For a long time there was no sound but the hoarse croaking of frogs from a nearby pond. The children waited quietly. Then suddenly Jim pointed across the grass.

"Fox!" he breathed. "Don't make a sound. He's just looking over the ground before he starts his hunt. If he hears us, he'll be gone in a flash."

Against the moonlit sky June could see a slim, motionless body. It was a red fox. His ears stood up, and his nose sniffed the air for scents of food or danger. But the wind blew too strongly to carry the scent of people to his keen nose.

After a last look around, the fox began to advance slyly through the tall grass.

"I'm going to try something," Jim muttered softly. "Don't move a muscle."

Quickly he lowered his head and drew his lips together. June almost shrieked aloud at the mouselike squeak that came from her brother's mouth.

Then she forgot her alarm as she watched the fox. He sat down and stared right in the direction of the children.

Jim squeaked again.

The fox came trotting toward them. His ears stood up stiffly, and his nose twitched.

Suddenly he hesitated and looked around him. He was now so close that June could see his whiskers jerking rapidly. The fox was trying hard to pick up the scent of the mouse. He was certain that the mouse was very near.

Just then there came a thump and a loud yell from the ground beside the log. The fox barked with fright and bolted.

"Oh-ooooo!" howled David. "I fell out of bed. Who moved my bed outdoors?"

Jim pulled David to his feet and dusted him off. David blinked in surprise.

"You're a fine one to go animal-watching!" June scolded. "You have been sleeping on that log for an hour. And you had to pick this minute to roll off and scare the fox!"

"What fox?" David mumbled sleepily. "All I saw was a skunk catching a mouse."

Jim laughed. "We may as well go home. No animal that heard David yell will come out of hiding tonight. But now that we know about this zoo without bars, we must come again. Next time, though, David must take a long nap before we come."

The Wild Colt's Lesson

War Paint was a wild colt whose spotted hide looked as if brushfuls of paint had been spilled all over it. With a herd of wild horses, he wandered over the broad western plains as free as the wind.

The favorite sport of the frisky colts was a kind of boxing. Standing up on their hind legs, the youngsters would paw at each other with their forefeet. This play helped them become sure-footed. It also taught them how to defend themselves in time of danger.

Occasionally during their play the lively animals would pause to snatch a mouthful of grass. Then back they would go again to their boxing.

When the colts tired of their sport, they would settle down to steady grazing close to the herd.

One day War Paint and his partner, Nosey, started off to explore a deep gully. They had not gone very far when War Paint heard his mother whinny to him. Nosey went on, but War Paint hesitated. Then Nosey looked back. He seemed to be saying, "Oh, come on. Let's see what's in this gully."

So War Paint paid no more attention to his mother's warning whinny. He pranced boldly after his partner.

The colts went a short distance into the gully. Then suddenly a stone came rattling down a bank. The startled animals whirled. There stood a prairie wolf, ready to pounce!

Instantly the terrified colts started back toward the herd, trying to seek escape up the rocky cliff. Nosey deserted his partner and bolted up the gully to safety.

War Paint started to follow Nosey. The wolf headed him off and lunged at his hind legs in fury.

The spotted colt dodged this way and that in terror. But the crafty wolf dodged, too. Once more the beast lunged furiously at the colt's hind legs. War Paint slashed out with his heels to defend himself.

War Paint saved his legs, but the wolf's powerful jaws scraped his side. Squealing with pain, the colt tried again to flee from the gully. His playful adventure had become a desperate fight for life.

Fiercely the killer sprang after the injured colt. War Paint was wild with terror. He was cornered again. The big wolf lunged a third time. Fortunately, War Paint leaped high in the air just as the wolf threw himself forward.

The wolf was so intent on his prey that he did not hear the pounding hoofs at the top of the gully. Suddenly a black thunderbolt shot down the side of the rocky cliff. With ears laid back and teeth bared, War Paint's mother plunged to his rescue.

Caught completely off guard, the wolf had no chance to escape. The enraged mare gave a lightninglike lunge and sank her teeth into the wolf's hide. Then with a quick toss of her head she cast the wolf into a big clump of sharp-thorned cactus. He lay quite still. Apparently he was badly injured.

The black mare's eyes gleamed with fury. Instantly she plunged into the cactus after the wolf. Her powerful forefeet were ready to slash the enemy and teach him the lesson he deserved. But just in time the wolf got to his feet and limped swiftly away.

War Paint's mother did not try to follow him. Instead, she turned to her trembling colt and whinnied. When the colt whinnied in reply, she nosed him over gently.

As soon as the mare found that War Paint was not badly injured, she snorted loudly as if to scold him. Then she gave him a little bite on his shoulder and pushed him gently on the forehead.

"There, my son," the mare seemed to be saying. "I hope that you have learned your lesson."

A Falls and a Fawn

"Isn't a waterfall the most beautiful thing in the world?" Joyce shouted to her brother.

"Well, a mountain is splendid, too," Phil replied. "But I guess nothing beats a waterfall for noise. If this fence weren't here, I could get really close to the falls."

"This fence keeps people from falling over the cliff," said Joyce. "So you stay here."

Phil suddenly pointed downward. "Look!" he cried. "See the fawn on those rocks!"

Joyce stared down at the mossy rocks on the bank near the base of the falls.

"Why, sure enough!" she exclaimed. "It's a baby fawn! See how still it's standing."

Just then a doe appeared in the bushes behind the rocks. With short, quick steps she advanced toward the rocks. Then she turned and hurried back into the shadows of the bushes.

After the doe had done this several times, Joyce cried, "Something must be wrong!"

"It sort of looks like it," Phil agreed. "That doe must be trying to get the fawn to follow her. I wonder why it just stands there."

"Maybe it can't get away!" Joyce cried. "Maybe it's caught in the rocks!"

"Here's where we could use an elevator," Phil remarked. "But say! There must be a trail down to the bottom of the falls. I'll ask Dad if we have time to go down to the fawn before lunch."

Phil ran quickly to a distant picnic table. Joyce waited by the railing, watching with pity the timid fawn and its worried mother.

Phil came panting back. "Dad is looking for a place to get drinking water," he said. "But Mother says it's all right if we hurry. I brought the rope that we tied around our picnic basket. We may need it."

Phil and Joyce soon spied the trail and started downward. At the trail's end they found themselves on the edge of a rushing stream. But they were on one side of the falls, while the fawn was on the other side. And between the fawn and the children was the whirlpool made by the water that came flooding down the cliff.

Just then the fawn noticed the children. It stood watching them with startled eyes.

"What shall we do now?" wailed Joyce.

"Well," said Phil, "we'll have to get over to the other side of the falls somehow. But we mustn't risk falling into the whirlpool. It's too dangerous."

"I know," said Joyce. "But how *can* we get across?"

Phil stepped closer to the wall of water that was roaring down into the stream and examined the rock behind it.

"Look!" he exclaimed. "This rock is all hollowed out behind the falls. See how it makes a little passageway!"

Joyce looked eagerly. Behind the waterfall was an opening like a low tunnel. The cliff made a wall on one side. The rushing falls made the other wall.

The children ducked their heads and went into the passageway. If they bent over just a little, they could walk easily along its rock floor. Directly behind the falls the path was perfectly dry and level.

Halfway through the narrow passageway Joyce stopped and stared out at the wall of water in front of her.

"Just think!" she cried. "We're behind
a waterfall! It sparkles like diamonds!"

"Just like a girl," Phil muttered. "Come
on, we have work to do."

"Just like a boy!" Joyce laughed as she
followed Phil through the passage.

When the children came out from behind
the falls, the tiny fawn remained motionless.
But as Phil and Joyce drew nearer, its eyes
rolled with terror.

"Its hoof is caught between two rocks,"
Joyce cried.

"I believe I can move this rock a little,"
Phil said as he knelt down by the fawn.

When he moved the rock, the fawn pulled its leg free and leaped into the stream.

"No, no!" Joyce shrieked. "You're going toward the whirlpool!"

Phil leaned out to grab the fawn, but it plunged still closer to the whirlpool.

"We'll have to do something quick!" cried Phil desperately. "He'll drown!"

"Use the rope!" Joyce yelled.

"I can tie a slipknot," Phil said, "but I'm not sure I can throw it around him."

Quickly he made a loop in the rope and tossed it at the struggling fawn. But the rope fell short and dropped into the water.

Three times Phil tried. Each time the rope fell short.

In a flash Phil pulled off his shoes and socks. He waded out in the shallow water near the rocks and tossed the rope again. This time the loop encircled the fawn's thin neck.

Gently Phil pulled the animal to the shore. Joyce knelt and held its trembling body while Phil took the rope from its neck.

"Now run to your mother," Joyce said.

As the animal bounded away, the children caught a glimpse of the doe. She had been waiting in the bushes all this time.

Just then the children heard a shout. It was their father, who was leaning over the railing high above them. When Joyce and Phil looked up, he pointed a finger at his open mouth.

"Food!" cried Phil, hurriedly putting on his socks and shoes. "I certainly can use some. How about you, Joyce?"

But his sister was already scrambling up the steep trail to hot dogs, potato chips, and chocolate pie.

Bushy Tail's Escape

One by one the pale stars appeared in the sky over the forest. The midsummer night was filled with soft, mysterious sounds as small woodland creatures crept cautiously out from their hiding places.

They were risking their lives in search of food. Silent-winged owls waited in the dark branches of the trees, ready to pounce on any mouse or wood rat that ventured forth. Weasels and foxes prowled the forest trails. They were preying on weaker animals that were unable to defend themselves.

Hidden underground in their den beneath an old stump, a father and mother chipmunk and their babies were sound asleep. Even Bushy Tail, the frisky one, lay quietly.

Occasionally sounds from the forest above came faintly into the burrow. Then the old chipmunks stirred uneasily in their sleep.

The doorway of the burrow was small, and the tunnel that led to the chipmunks' den was long and narrow. So the chipmunks had little to dread from most night prowlers.

But the weasel is one prowler from which chipmunks are never safe. His body is so slim that he can squeeze his way into the deepest part of a chipmunk's burrow. His sharp eyes can see the slightest movement in the grass. And his nose is as keen as the nose of a fox.

Tonight, while the chipmunks were asleep, danger was very near. A weasel was slyly making his way toward their burrow.

Presently the father chipmunk woke up. Something warned him of danger, and he started up the tunnel at once.

In an instant the old chipmunk was at the burrow door. Here he paused and listened intently. He heard no sound, and at first he saw nothing alarming.

Then suddenly on the dim hillside below him Father Chipmunk's eyes caught a slight movement. A slim, dark form was sneaking through the shadows and moving toward the burrow. One glance told the chipmunk of his danger. That long, slim body belonged to his most dreaded enemy—the weasel.

Father Chipmunk fled back down the tunnel to the den. There he turned and looked up the narrow passageway. At the entrance a faint light shone. The sly weasel could enter the den only through this passage. As long as the chipmunk could see that round patch of light, he and his family would be secure from their enemy.

But in a moment the small patch of light was blacked out. The dreaded weasel had found the opening into the burrow!

The old chipmunk did not hesitate. After barking a warning to his family, he fled up a back tunnel to a secret door. Through this door escape was possible.

Mother Chipmunk and the little ones woke in terror and scurried after him. In their haste to flee through the secret door, they scratched and clawed each other frantically.

Meanwhile, the weasel was trying to enter the front door of the burrow. The entrance was tight, even for his slim body.

Squirming and twisting, the crafty weasel finally managed to force his way down into the tunnel. His greedy eyes shone cruelly as his keen nose caught the scent of the chipmunks' tracks. That scent promised to lead him to a tasty meal.

But when he reached the den, it was empty! The chipmunks had fled. Only their tracks to the secret tunnel now remained. Eagerly sniffing these tracks, the weasel forced his way toward the secret door.

Bushy Tail had been the last chipmunk to escape from the tunnel. When he found himself outside, he was filled with fresh terror. His family had vanished!

Then the little chipmunk saw the weasel coming out the secret door. Bushy Tail ran swiftly toward an old hollow tree. Among its roots were many familiar hiding places. If only he could reach those roots in time!

Suddenly Bushy Tail looked back. What he saw increased his panic. Close behind him two small, greedy eyes gleamed through the darkness. The crafty weasel was near and would soon pounce upon him!

All at once the silence of the night was broken by the fierce hunting cry of a great horned owl. The bird swooped from a giant oak nearby. Straight as an arrow it dived at those two gleaming eyes. There was a rustling in the shadows. Then all was still. The dreaded weasel would prowl no more, for the owl had seized its prey.

Bushy Tail was safe now as he bolted for the roots of the hollow tree. At a burrow entrance his nose caught a familiar scent. Pausing, he twitched his tail happily. Bushy Tail had found his family!

Billy and the Loons

As another fish flopped into the bottom of the canoe, Billy Grayson's eyes shone.

"That's a good catch, isn't it, Chief?" he asked his companion.

The Indian guide's face wrinkled into a smile as he looked at the boy's eager face.

"You're doing all right, Billy," he said in his soft voice. "And when we get ashore, I'll show you how to clean your fish."

"Will I be a woodsman then?" asked ten-year-old Billy hopefully.

"You'll be on the way, son, on the way," Chief told him encouragingly.

Billy fished in silence for a while. Then he asked, "What else do I have to do before I'm a real woodsman?"

"Well," his companion replied, "you really should sleep outdoors at least once. Sleeping on the ground toughens you up.

"It's nice to sleep by a lake. You hear the waves talking and the wind whispering through the pines. You might even hear the loons calling before you drop off to sleep.

"Then," the guide's soft voice went on, "if you wake up very early, you might see the loons dance. Lots of woodsmen have tried but failed to see the loons dance. But you might be one who does."

"I'll ask Dad when we go ashore if I may sleep out," Billy said. "Do you think he'll let me?"

The Indian smiled. "Your dad is a wise man," he replied. "He will say 'Yes.'"

With a quiet stroke of the paddle, Chief turned the canoe toward the spot where the Graysons were camping. In a space partly surrounded by tall trees, Billy could see the ring of stones for a fire. Soon Chief would be cooking the fish that Billy had caught.

As soon as he ran ashore, the boy asked his father's permission to sleep outdoors. Mr. Grayson agreed at once. Mrs. Grayson said, "Oh, Billy!" But she quickly added, "Be sure to take enough blankets, Son."

The boy was almost too excited to eat his supper. But the fish he had caught tasted delicious. He managed to eat an amazing number.

At dusk Billy shouldered his blanket roll. He was eager to start on his adventure.

"I'll go and help Billy find a good place to sleep," the Indian guide told Mr. and Mrs. Grayson.

Leading the way, the Indian walked until
he found a little hollow under a great pine.
The lake shore was close by, and the water
lapped gently against the rocks. Soon the
blankets were spread, and Billy rolled himself up in them.

"Would you like to keep the lantern?" the
guide asked.

Billy wanted very much to keep it. But
he shook his head.

The Indian looked at Billy silently for a
minute. "Good boy!" he said. And taking
the lantern, he moved quietly away.

"How quiet it is!" thought Billy, looking upward at a star that twinkled through the branches of the pine tree. Then a breeze whispered, and the waves broke sleepily on the rocky shore. Far away a loon called. The boy smiled and was soon fast asleep.

Billy woke suddenly to the dim, gray light of dawn. A mist lay over the lake. Above him the pine needles dripped water. He had never been awake so early before, and the swirling mist made everything seem strange. He was not exactly afraid, but he was glad he had not awakened in the dark.

Suddenly from the water nearby came a loon's loud cry. Then another and another could be heard. The cries sounded like wild laughter.

Billy rolled over quietly. He did not want to risk frightening the loons away. Now he could see the lake without even raising his head. How near the loons had sounded! He peered out into the swirling mist, wishing he could see better.

Gradually the mist rose higher. There, right before Billy's eyes, were the loons.

"One, two, six, eight, ten!" Billy counted aloud. "I wish Dad and Mother and Chief could see those birds!"

Again wild laughter rose from the water. Against the mist, Billy could see the loons' thin necks and pointed bills.

As the boy watched eagerly, he saw the big birds form into two lines opposite each other, about ten or eleven feet apart.

"Will they dance?" wondered Billy. "Am I really going to see the loons dance?"

For a moment the opposite lines of birds remained quietly facing each other across the lane of water. Then the two loons at one end moved toward each other and turned to face the lane.

Suddenly these two birds rose half out of the lake and swept down the lane. Their black wings beat the water, and their feet churned it to foam. At the foot of the line the two birds took their places. Afterwards they filled the air with their laughter.

Now the next pair churned down the lane and laughed wildly. The dance was repeated again and again, while Billy hardly ventured to breathe.

Then there was a sudden crackling rustle above him, like the rustle of stiff silk. An eagle swooped down over the misty lake. At once the loons dived. The eagle flew off, and only the foaming water was left.

Billy lay very still for a long time. But the loons did not reappear on the surface of the lake. After a while Billy rolled up his blankets and started back toward the camp. He walked very quietly, for he did not want to wake his parents.

As the boy approached the tents, he could smell smoke. Sitting by a crackling fire was the Indian guide.

"Oh, Chief!" Billy whispered. "Did you hear the loons? I saw them! I saw their dance!"

Chief turned slowly, his eyes intent and serious. "I saw the dance, too, son. Don't ever forget it. It may be a long time until you see that dance again."

"And I slept outdoors by myself!" Billy cried. "Am I a real woodsman yet?"

"I believe so," the Indian told him. "I believe you're a grown-up woodsman now!"

Wilderness Partners

A huge grizzly bear sat perfectly still in a shallow stream. His eyes were fixed on the clear water swirling about his forepaws. The bear ate many kinds of food. But he chose only what he considered the tastiest. And of all the foods that he ate, he liked fish the best. Because he had roamed the wilderness for so long, he knew when the trout chose to swim upriver to another pool. He knew also that they passed through the stream right where he was sitting. It was their highway between two pools.

Now a large trout was swimming toward him. The bear raised his head. His keen eyes followed the trout's gleaming back as the fish fought its way upstream.

Nearer and nearer came the trout. Then suddenly its way was blocked by the bear's solid form. The trout paused. An instant later it lunged forward through the water swirling around the grizzly's forepaws.

With amazing speed for anything so large, the grizzly slapped the water with his huge forepaw. The force of the slap caused a spout of water to squirt upward. The trout rose with the water.

It landed on a rock by the stream. As the grizzly started toward it, the nearby bushes parted. Out walked a woolly puppy. His eyes were alert, and his ears stood up sharply. His face, with its gray and white markings, showed that he was a Husky.

Without heeding the big grizzly, the puppy pounced on the flopping fish. He pinned it down with his forepaws and sank his sharp teeth into its smooth sides. Then, walking backward, he began to drag the trout toward the bushes.

Over the big grizzly's face came a look of complete astonishment. Then his surprise turned to anger. With a snort the enraged animal scrambled up the bank. He halted just before he reached the puppy.

The puppy had stopped, too. Seemingly he had sensed the bear's anger and had dropped the stolen fish.

Now the Husky moved back a few steps. His tail twitching, he watched the bear sniff at the gasping trout.

The grizzly bit the big trout in half and swallowed the part with the head. Then he turned to the other half. He bit it off just above the tail. The tail he left lying on the bank.

It looked as if the bear were offering the pup a reward for not eating his catch. But actually the grizzly did not like fish tails.

Finished with his meal, the bear shuffled over to sniff at the Husky.

The puppy sat perfectly still. Somehow he sensed that now he had nothing to fear from the grizzly. He was right. Although the bear was a terrible enemy when angered, most of the time he was friendly. His good nature sprang from the fact that he was so much stronger than all the other wilderness animals. After a few moments the grizzly ambled back to the stream.

The hungry pup gobbled up the fish tail and lay down to wait. If the bear caught more trout, the Husky would have more tails to eat. He would have a good meal before he continued his search for the wild mother Husky from whom he had wandered.

The Magic Coat

Tawny, a baby mountain lion, first opened his eyes in a dusky den on Mount Grizzly. His brownish-yellow fur was sprinkled with dark spots, and he was as soft and round-eyed as any kitten.

Like all kittens, Tawny did not want his mother to wash him. "Mew!" he cried in his small, high-pitched voice. And he kicked as hard as he knew how.

But Tawny's mother held him fast in her forepaws as she licked the warm milk from his whiskers. "Mmmmm," she purred.

Tawny squirmed and twisted, but it was useless. His mother went on cleaning and smoothing every part of his plump body.

Then came his sister Leone's turn. His twin had the same black spots on her back. She had the same black tip to her nose, and the same black rings encircled her tail. But Leone was smaller than Tawny.

The two kittens lived in a cave on a steep ledge. At first they were too weak even to walk. They had to shove themselves along on their stomachs with their hind legs. But soon they were strong enough to play games.

"Ffft!" Tawny would call in cat language.

"Ffft!" Leone would reply.

Then the mischievous kittens pretended to fight. With backs humped and tails bushed out in make-believe anger, they would leap at each other. Away they would go, rolling in a furry ball.

One day Tawny's mother was out hunting, and Leone was asleep in the cave. Tawny sat at the mouth of the cave, lazily enjoying the sunshine. His eyelids were almost closed. Suddenly they snapped open alertly.

Just out of Tawny's reach was a butterfly. Tawny leaped for it. But he did not catch the butterfly. Instead, the kitten turned completely over. Missing the ledge, he pitched downward to the ground below.

The earth was soft and springy with pine needles. Tawny was not hurt by the fall, but he could not get back up into the den. The ledge was too high for him to jump up on it. Nor could he dig his claws into the hard surface to climb up.

Frightened, Tawny crouched in the shade of some low bushes. Then he saw a coyote sneaking toward him. The animal's hungry look increased Tawny's terror.

"Ffftt!" hissed Tawny, ready to fight for his life. But the coyote only crept nearer. His greedy eyes never left the little hump of fur crouched at the foot of the ledge.

All at once the furry hump lunged forward. The kitten startled the larger animal with a stinging slap of his paw.

Uttering a loud "Yiii!" the coyote backed out of reach. Instantly Tawny scrambled up a nearby tree trunk. Trembling, he clung to the rough bark while the coyote crouched below, watching the kitten intently.

But soon poor Tawny felt his claws giving way under the weight of his fat body. As the coyote gazed at him hungrily, he began to slide down the tree trunk.

Then, not far away, Tawny could hear his mother coming. He gave a wail of despair. His cry was small and high-pitched, but it reached his mother's ears.

There was a flash of red-brown fur. The big mountain lion was rushing to her baby's rescue. She reached the tree just as the coyote was jumping up toward Tawny.

"Grrr!" she threatened, growling deep in her throat.

The coyote fled, his tail between his legs.

Quickly Tawny's mother looked her baby over. Then she picked him up by the loose skin on the back of his neck. She carried him in her mouth to the foot of the ledge.

The door of her den was a few feet above. But with little effort she leaped the entire distance. Grabbing the edge of the rock with her great forepaws, she drew herself up over it. She did not drop Tawny until she was far back in the snug cave.

One bright morning the mother cat taught
her babies a game. Tawny and Leone were
napping just outside the back opening to the
cave. When they woke, their mother was
nowhere in sight. At least the two kittens
could not find her.

This was very strange. Sniffing around,
they could smell their mother's warm fur.
They stood listening, their wee tails twitching. Surely they could hear her breathing.

Tawny was confused. His eyes searched
the ground. Then he looked up. What had
become of his mother?

"Grrr!" called the mother cat, rolling the sound in her throat. The call came from a branch above Tawny. The leaves stirred. Now the kittens could see their mother!

There she lay, crouching along the limb of a large tree. Her white underside was pressed close against the bark. And it was almost impossible to see her brownish fur among the brown branches. It was just as though she had a magic coat that hid her.

"Mmm!" purred the mother cat, watching her youngsters' surprise.

She would play this game with her babies many times. By and by they would learn that they, too, had magic coats to protect them from threatening enemies.

But now it was time to eat. The great mountain lion leaped to the ground to see what she could catch for supper.

Tawny scampered back into the cave with his twin. He was still too young to hunt. But he would learn. Soon he would be able to seek his own food. And he would learn how to keep from being preyed upon by the other wild animals.

Willie the Moose

Willie shoved his head around the corner of a low log building that stood in a snow-covered clearing. The moose peered at the spot he had just left so hurriedly.

A moment before he had tried to drive off the Clayton family's two frisky young dogs by kicking at them. Unhappily his flying hoof had hit Mr. Clayton's leg.

Now from behind the logging-camp stable Willie could see the lumberman rubbing his leg and glaring about. Herbert and Kitty Clayton were running from the family cabin toward their father.

"This is the last straw!" Mr. Clayton told the children angrily. "We'll simply have to get rid of Willie."

"But, Dad," argued Kitty, "it was just an accident. Willie didn't mean to kick you."

"Of course not," Herbert added. "We saw the dogs bothering him. You just happened to be in the way of Willie's hoof."

But Mr. Clayton was determined to get rid of the moose. "We've no place to cage him up, and he's too big and strong to run loose like a pet any longer. No telling when he might injure somebody seriously."

Kitty's forehead wrinkled with concern.

"What do you intend to do with Willie?" she asked anxiously.

"I'll just have to run that moose off into the woods," her father answered.

"Oh, no!" Kitty wailed in despair. "Poor Willie!"

Followed by the children, Mr. Clayton limped toward the cabin. "Herbert," he said, "remember now. I want you and Kitty to stay away from Willie. I'll get rid of him as soon as I can."

The Claytons had found Willie in the woods when he was a helpless, week-old calf. Ever since they had treated him kindly. Herbert and Kitty had fed and cared for him. They had spent most of their time with him when they were not attending the country school two miles away.

But as the moose grew older, he seemed to take charge of the children. He never let them out of his sight as they swam in the lake or picked berries or roamed through the woods.

Now the moose's young charges seemed to be deserting him. Puzzled, Willie watched them go to their cabin. Then he ambled off toward the camp kitchen. The door was shut against the bitter cold, but even outside the smell of food was sweet and tempting.

The moose nosed the latch until he finally lifted it. Then he butted the door with his antlers, and it swung open.

Charlie, the logging-camp cook, was making flapjacks. "Hi, Willie!" shouted the cook. "Have some of your favorite food!" With that Charlie tossed a flapjack at the moose.

Willie gobbled up the flapjack and waited in the doorway for more.

Charlie tossed him several more flapjacks. Finally the cook said, "That's all, Willie. Now get out!"

"Moo-oo-oooo!" Willie bellowed.

"I'll *moo* you!" Charlie said. Picking up a dishpan full of water, he flung the water right in Willie's face.

"Get out!" yelled the cook. "Go before you eat up all the family's lunch!"

Willie backed out the door so fast that he sat down. Before he could get on his feet, the water dripping down his nose and chin had frozen into long, icy whiskers.

The next day Mr. Clayton tied one end of a rope around Willie's neck. He fastened the other end to his car and drove off along a logging trail. The children watched sadly as Willie was swallowed up by the forest.

Mile after mile the moose followed along at the end of the rope, his long legs churning like a windmill. At last he grew tired and began to fight the rope that encircled his neck. As the automobile bounced over a small pit in the trail, the moose gave an extra hard pull. The rope broke, and Willie regained his freedom.

He bounded off among the trees and ran until Mr. Clayton was far behind. Then the moose lay down and took a nap. When he woke, he felt hungry and lonesome. So he began walking toward the Clayton camp.

Suddenly he stopped and sniffed. There was a smell of flapjacks in the air!

Following his nose, he walked on until he almost stumbled upon a tent skillfully hidden by brushwood. Around a fire three men were sitting. They were all gobbling up stacks of delicious-smelling flapjacks.

Overcome with hunger, Willie mooed loudly and ran straight toward the men. At his unexpected appearance, they dropped everything and scattered into the woods.

Willie immediately ate up every flapjack in sight. Then he ambled on toward home.

He had a long way to go. But even though this part of the forest was strange to him, he managed to keep on the right trail.

When he was half a mile from the Clayton camp, he noticed a peculiar scarlet glow in the darkening sky above the trees. The red glow broadened as Willie stared.

Now the moose could smell burning logs. He ran bellowing to the bunkhouse. Then he sped to the Clayton cabin and set up an unearthly noise.

There were cries of "Fire! The stable's on fire!" as the loggers streamed from the bunkhouse. Mr. Clayton quickly joined them. Finally Herbert and Kitty came rushing out, buttoning on their heavy coats.

"Why, Willie is back!" cried Kitty. She and Herbert patted him fondly.

With the moose standing beside them, the two children watched as their father and his loggers fought the fire.

After the fire was out, Mr. Clayton said, "It's lucky that the blaze was discovered so soon."

"It was Willie who discovered the fire," Charlie said.

"Willie!" exclaimed Mr. Clayton.

"Yes," answered Charlie. "It was Willie's bellowing that gave the alarm."

"Well," said Herbert, "this proves that we need Willie here. He would make a splendid fire chief."

Mr. Clayton grinned. "I'll have to change my mind about Willie," he admitted. "He's certainly won the right to stay with us."

The next day the moose strutted about the camp with a large sign encircling his neck. The sign said, "Willie Clayton, Fire Chief."

A Dangerous Surprise

The mother sea otter was on the alert. She held herself straight up in the water. One third of her glossy brown body rose above the waving blue-green surface of the rock-walled cove. Although the water was deep, she stood so straight that it looked as if she were standing on the bottom.

Occasionally she twitched her black nose and white whiskers. Her eyes followed her plump, woolly baby intently as he practiced swimming for the first time alone.

136

Adapted by permission of the publisher, J. B. Lippincott Company, from *The Last of the Sea Otters* by Harold McCracken. Copyright, 1942, by Harold McCracken.

Learning to swim was like a game to the baby sea otter. He paddled his short front legs furiously. He wiggled his whole body as he splashed the water into foam with his hind feet and tail.

Every time his face went under water he snorted and shook his head hard. Once he tried to dive but came up choking. With a little look of fright in his eyes he rolled over on his back for a brief rest while he recovered his breath.

The days passed swiftly for the little sea otter. He was always learning something. Every day he learned something new that he could do or should not do. Nearly every day he saw some new creature that lived in the sea or flew in the air.

But his world was still a very small one. It did not go beyond the rocky cliffs that walled the cove where he and his mother lived.

Swimming under water was the young sea otter's favorite sport. Everything appeared different in the strange world beneath the surface.

One day the little otter was gliding gracefully under water past the rocky sides of the
cove. He poked his black nose exploringly
along the ledges.

On one ledge crawled an odd-looking crab.
Its arms were almost as long as the baby
otter's whole body. It moved them slowly,
as if it were tired.

The sea otter stopped for a moment to
watch this queer creature. Then he shot up
to the surface briefly to get a fresh breath
of air. He tried to jump clear out of the
water as he had seen his mother do.
Then down he went again
to find something else.

There was only one place in the entire cove where he was forbidden to go. This was around a large ledge that overhung the water near a small beach. The top of the ledge was smooth and level. To the young sea otter it looked like the nicest place in all the cove to lie and sleep.

When he was younger, he had crawled out on this ledge several times. Each time his mother had barked a stern warning. Then she had come to him as fast as she could. Grabbing him in her teeth, she had carried him away quickly. As she put him down, she had bumped him very roughly with her snout.

"You stay away from there!" she seemed to be saying.

The little otter had never seen anything dangerous near this forbidden ledge. But his mother's warnings had made him curious and doubly eager to go back. There must be something very unusual there. It was probably under the water.

The otter determined to go to the ledge at his first chance.

One day the mother sea otter was floating on her back out in the center of the cove. She was playing with a bunch of seaweed. Purring contentedly, she tossed the seaweed into the air, first with one paw, then with the other.

When the young otter saw that his mother was not watching, he took a deep breath. Then he dived and swam quickly toward the forbidden place.

As he glided along through the water, he met a school of small, flat fish that had wandered into the cove. They were about the size of his hind feet. Occasionally he had seen these fish before. He had always tried to catch one then. Now he scarcely noticed them.

Eagerly he approached the big ledge. His little nose pointed straight ahead. His eyes tried to pierce the dark underwater shadows before him. Then his heart began to beat fast, and he slowed his speed.

Once the youngster faltered and started to double back. But he saw nothing frightening, and he went closer.

It was like a cave beneath the overhang-
ing ledge. To the youngster it looked like
a good place to explore. But it was very
dark. He swam up almost to the entrance.
Peering inside, he thought he saw something
move.

Suddenly the whole cave seemed to come
alive. The most startling thing the young
otter had ever seen rushed out upon him.
The foaming water appeared to be filled with
long wiggling arms lined with suckers. In
the center of these arms was a shapeless
body with two great eyes at the top. The
arms shot out at the young sea otter as if
to throw themselves around him.

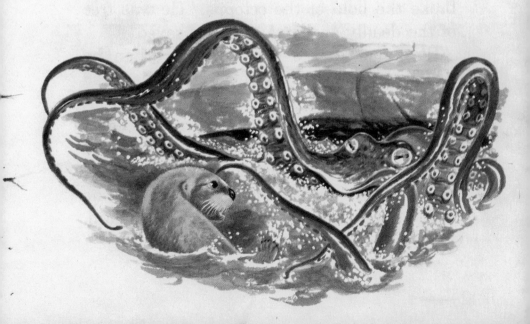

It was an octopus. For a long time this octopus had been waiting in its underwater cave for something like a baby sea otter to swim near. Now it was ready to grab its prey for a wonderful feast.

The frightened otter whirled in the water to make a desperate dash for safety. But one of the octopus' long arms slipped around the back part of his body. Frantically the otter struggled to get free as the octopus tried to fasten the suckers of its arm upon him. Fortunately, the thick, woolly hair on the otter's body prevented the suckers from taking a firm hold.

Suddenly, with a quick movement, the otter broke the hold of the octopus. He was free of the deadly suckers! He was saved!

He swam to the surface faster than he had ever traveled before. When his head came up into the air, he sped to his mother.

From his frightened look she sensed what had happened. She nosed him over to make certain he was uninjured. Then she rolled over on her back again. She was sure he would never go to the forbidden ledge again.

Gray Wing and Nika

From their wilderness home in the North flew a wedge of splendid big Canada geese. They were winging their way southward for the winter.

Led by a wise old gander, they flew over mountains and the silvery ribbon of a wide river. Straight to a forest-edged lake the gander piloted his flock of sixty geese. This lake had always been as secure for them as their far-off northern home. Each year the birds rested here for a day or so. Then they flew on to their southern feeding grounds.

Near the middle of the wedge of soaring Canadas flew Gray Wing, a splendid young gander. His back and wings were darker than those of his companions. In the rays of the western sun his glossy feathers shone like satin.

Flying near Gray Wing was graceful Nika, his mate.

When the geese were directly over the lake, the wedge spread out. The birds began to settle for the night upon the calm water.

The geese woke at dawn. Paddling close to shore, they began to feed on the wild rice, which was plentiful that autumn season. Gray Wing and Nika swam about with the other geese, concealed by the morning mist. The gray birds were fearless, for they had never been bothered on this peaceful lake.

Slowly the sky lightened. The mist began to rise, and the shoreline appeared. There, concealed in the reeds, were two men with guns. As the fog lifted, they saw the flock of splendid geese.

The hunters lost no time. Instantly two shots burst out. A great outcry rose from the startled geese. With a heavy rustling of wings they started upward in desperate flight.

There was a second burst of shot. Now the geese mounted rapidly. Above their outcry rose the call of their leader, the wise old gander.

High overhead the birds circled. Then they headed southward through the protecting mist. Of the sixty geese, all but three were in the wedge. One of these was Nika.

At the first shots one goose had flopped head downward into the water, a huddle of limp feathers. Another bird had faltered and dropped when the guns had blazed away the second time.

At that moment Nika, rising swiftly from the lake, had felt a blow on her left wing. This was followed by a sharp pain. Nika had faltered, then steadied herself. Now she was attempting to beat her way upward.

But she could not reach the swiftly flying wedge. She called out to the flock. Only Gray Wing, her mate, heeded her wild cry. Looking back, he discovered that Nika was missing from the wedge.

Gray Wing uttered an answering cry. He turned, left the flying wedge, and swooped down toward Nika. By this time she was barely above the treetops, for the pain in her injured wing was increasing.

The rest of the geese soared on. From the misty sky the honking of the flock came back, high and clear. Then the cries grew fainter and fainter. Gradually the sounds died away.

Soon Nika's strength was spent. So she and her mate dropped down to a little pond, where the reeds and rice concealed them.

Fortunately, only Nika's wing was injured, but she was weak from the pain. When she had recovered some of her strength, both geese began to feed on the wild rice.

It was noon when a few tame ducks from a nearby farm came to the pond. They were marching in a single line behind a handsome green-headed drake. Gray Wing and Nika watched the ducks and the drake wade out into the water. Presently the northern birds ventured forth from the rice stalks and reeds near the shore.

As the geese swam out to join the tame
fowls, they were suddenly frightened by a
herd of cows approaching the pond to drink.
Gray Wing rose up. But Nika's attempt to
follow was in vain. Her injured wing could
not bear her weight.

Gray Wing wheeled and flew back to Nika.
Again they hid in the reeds near the shore.

Young Frank Gordon, who drove the cows, was much excited. He hurried back to the farm where he lived with his Aunt Lizzie and Uncle Peter. Breathlessly he told them about the two wild geese. When Aunt Lizzie Gordon heard her nephew's report, she said that the visitors were not to be harmed.

The next day Frank took some corn from the crib. He scattered it beside the pond where the two strangers could find it. As he watched the geese eating the grain, he wished he could make pets of them.

Gray Wing and Nika remained among the rice and reeds while Nika's wing mended. Gradually it grew stronger. But Nika could not yet fly. After frequent attempts to lead her away, Nika's faithful mate always came back to her.

One morning the two big Canadas heard a distant honking. A large flock of geese was flying southward. Nika tried to rise and join them. But she could not. Faithful Gray Wing did not desert her. He stayed with her, ready to help her and to protect her from harm.

The last days of autumn passed swiftly. Then one night a storm swept in from the northwest. It was followed by a day of icy rain and bitter cold. Aunt Lizzie Gordon thought immediately of the big gray geese. They must be sheltered from the fury of the winter storms. So Frank went out and left a trail of corn on the ground. In this way the birds were coaxed into a pen.

The geese no longer had their freedom, but they were safe with the other fowls. As the season advanced, they seemed to grow used to their pen. Frequently they were allowed to run loose in the barnyard. They came fearlessly at Frank's call.

Uncle Peter grumbled because the geese ate so much grain. Once he suggested roast goose for Christmas. But Aunt Lizzie gave him such a scolding that he quickly insisted it was only a joke. And that was his last remark about roast goose.

One morning there was a wild honking in the barnyard. Nika was trying her wings! For fifty yards she circled upward. Then, faltering, she swooped to the ground.

By the end of winter Nika had recovered
from her wound and was able to fly again.
On the first warm spring day she and Gray
Wing grew restless. They were longing for
the freedom of their northern home.

One day a familiar call came from the sky.
A large wedge of Canada geese was flying
directly overhead. They were returning from
their winter home in the South.

Their cries urged Gray Wing and Nika to
join their flight to freedom. The two geese
hissed in their pen and beat their splendid
wings against the wire. But it was in vain.
They could not escape.

Three days later a big wind storm struck suddenly during the night. Much damage was caused on the farm by the harsh blasts. Big branches were torn from the trees, and shingles were blown off the farmhouse roof. The weather vane was twisted off the barn.

When Frank Gordon woke the next morning, he heard the fowls making a great deal of noise. He dressed quickly and ran to the shed where the Canadas were kept at night. There Frank saw that the wind had blown a big tree limb against the door, smashing it completely. The geese had escaped.

Then far overhead the boy heard a faint honking. Immediately there were answering cries from Gray Wing and Nika. He looked up just in time. Upward swept the two big birds to join the wedge of Canadas. Up, up they went—flying free at last.

Famous Americans
of Other Times

George Grows Up

"George," called Mrs. Washington one day from the farmhouse door. "I want you to help me clean out the storehouse. It hasn't been done since your father died."

The storehouse was a small building, near the kitchen, where many things that were not used every day were kept. Cleaning it seemed a tedious job to the lively thirteen-year-old boy, but George Washington did as his mother asked.

In a dark corner of the storehouse, George found something strange made of iron rods. He examined it closely.

"What is this?" he asked his mother.

When she saw what he was holding, she said, "That's your father's surveying chain. Did you never see it before? Your father used it to measure the land he bought. He wanted to make sure that all the boundary lines were actually right."

"May I keep this?" George asked.

"If you like," answered Mrs. Washington. Then she hurried away on an errand.

"I will talk with Lawrence about learning surveying," George thought.

Lawrence Washington, who was George's older half-brother, lived at Mount Vernon. Shortly after George's fourteenth birthday the lad had a chance to go to Mount Vernon. As soon as he could arrange it, he talked to his brother alone.

"I would like to give up school and learn surveying, Lawrence," George said. "School is tedious and boring. I want to learn what I need for a *man's* work."

"I have been thinking about your future," Lawrence replied. "Your mother will not permit you to go to school in England as I did. But perhaps you could go to sea."

"To sea!" George cried. "Oh, Lawrence, that would be wonderful! But will Mother let me go?" he added in sudden dismay.

"I will ride back with you tomorrow and ask her," Lawrence said.

The next day he asked Mrs. Washington's permission for George to go to sea.

She settled the matter at once. "George is not to go!" she said firmly.

For a time George was disappointed. But at last he forgot about going to sea. He did not forget, however, about wanting to learn surveying.

One day George learned that an excellent surveyor, Mr. Byrne, lived in a nearby town.

"He might teach me," the boy thought.

The next day George went to Mr. Byrne's house. His knock was answered at once by a friendly-looking man.

"I'm looking for Surveyor Byrne," George announced.

"You have found him," the man answered with a smile. Then he motioned for George to enter.

"I am George Washington. Perhaps you knew my father," said George.

"So I did," Mr. Byrne replied. "I helped your father with several surveys. But that was some time ago."

"Yes, sir," George replied politely. "And now I want to be a surveyor, too. Would you teach me? I can figure very well, and I can draw a good map."

"Surveying is not all a gentleman's work," Mr. Byrne told him. "You'd have hours of tramping in the mud, climbing mountains, and wading shallow creeks. You'd hardly care for that."

"I like the outdoors, sir," George said. "What you say makes me want to learn all the more."

Mr. Byrne made up his mind quickly. "All right, George," he said. "Come tomorrow. Wear your top boots. You'll need them."

"Shall I bring my chain?" George asked.

"No," said Mr. Byrne, "you'll use mine."

From that time on George went on many
surveying trips with Mr. Byrne. George
learned to measure the boundaries of a piece
of land and to set out corner poles or use
trees as boundary markers.

He learned to draw maps of the boundaries
he had measured, showing all the rivers and
creeks. His drawing was always neat and
his lettering clear. Sometimes he would just
describe a boundary line in writing. The
line might be between a maple tree and an
oak, or between two spruces and an apple
tree.

When George was almost sixteen, William Fairfax, who lived near Mount Vernon, had a visitor from England. It was his cousin, Lord Fairfax. He owned thousands of acres of wilderness land in the West.

One morning when George was at Mount Vernon, he and Lawrence rode over to call on Lord Fairfax. They found him striding excitedly up and down the room. The pages of a letter in his hand shook as he walked.

"People are moving onto my land without paying for it!" he cried angrily. "They say that the land is vacant and belongs to any-one who wants it."

"You cannot do anything about it until you have your land surveyed," William advised. "You must know your boundary lines."

"Then let's make a survey," snapped the land owner. It was decided to do so at once.

"I hear that George is doing well with his surveying," William Fairfax told Lawrence. "Why not have him accompany the surveying party?"

Turning to the boy, William asked, "How about it, George?"

George's eyes gleamed. "I should like it very much, sir," he answered.

The surveying party left on their trip in the month of March. In charge was one of the best surveyors in Virginia. George's work was to describe the boundary lines in writing. His earlier training proved to be a great help to the party.

George was sorry when the five-week trip was ended. There was a thrill about the wilderness that he had never known before. He wondered how and when he would take such a journey again.

After the survey, George was recognized as a grown-up among the men around Mount Vernon. They asked his advice about the new wilderness land and discovered that he had noticed more about the soil than had the head surveyor. Now when the men talked about land, George joined in.

"I should like to own land in the West," Lawrence remarked at dinner one day.

"What does land sell for, George?" Lord Fairfax, who was a dinner guest, inquired.

"Oh, the price is cheap," George replied. "You can get a hundred acres for about six or seven pounds in English money."

The talk soon changed to soil and crops. About these, too, George knew a great deal.

After Lord Fairfax had gone, Lawrence put his hand on George's shoulder.

"You know, George," he said, "I've been sorry that you were not sent to school in England. But I begin to see that what you have learned here in Virginia may be worth more than what many other young men learn abroad. Virginia has a great future. And I expect you to have a big part in it."

The Boy Hunter

Daniel Boone was only ten when he asked his father for a gun.

"I reckon you're a little young for that," drawled his father. "You'll have to wait a couple of years longer."

While George Washington was learning to be a surveyor in Virginia, Daniel was growing up in a neighboring region. Like George, Daniel lived on a farm. But the Boone farm was on the edge of a thick forest.

Daniel had loved the forest as long as he could remember. When he was little more than a baby, he tramped through the woods while his father and older brothers hunted game for the family's table. At the age of ten Daniel knew the forest almost as well as he knew his own barnyard.

To Daniel two years seemed a long time to wait for a rifle. So he made himself a hunting weapon. He uprooted a slender tree and sharpened one end of it to a point. At the very first chance he got, he started off into the woods with his homemade weapon.

The boy did not come home empty-handed. He brought a couple of wild birds.

"Oh!" cried Mrs. Boone. "They'll make a fine supper for us. How did you manage to get them, Dan?"

"With this," answered Daniel. Proudly he held up the weapon he had made.

Daniel had little time to spend hunting with his new weapon. He had many chores and duties at home. But whenever he found an opportunity, the lad would slip off into the woods.

There Daniel learned many things that he could not learn in school. For one thing, he learned to read signs. By looking closely at the ground or brush, he could tell whether some wild animal had passed that way lately. He could even tell what kind of animal it was and track it to its hiding place.

He could also tell from the appearance of footprints whether a white man or an Indian had been roaming the forest.

Two years passed. At last the day came when Daniel's father provided him with a rifle. The lad was delighted. Now, more than ever, he tried to find time to go off into the woods. He soon became so skillful with his gun that he was praised far and wide as a hunter.

One November morning Daniel finished his chores quickly and shouldered his precious rifle. He had decided to go hunting.

Calling to his favorite dog, Daniel started into the woods. The boy's family was not worried to see him go off alone. They were used to his hunting trips, and the game he brought home was welcome. They supposed that he would be back by sunset. But darkness fell, and Daniel was still absent.

At supper Mr. Boone said, "Well, I reckon Dan can take care of himself."

"Yes," agreed the boy's mother. "He'll be back by tomorrow."

But he was not. When Daniel was still absent on the second day, his family began to be concerned. Late in the afternoon a searching party started off into the woods.

The searchers soon found the trail of the missing lad. A short time later they lost it. The boys in the party shouted, and the men fired their rifles, hoping that Daniel would answer. But they heard nothing.

At dusk one of the party caught sight of a distant plume of smoke. The searchers hurried toward it.

Guided by the smoke, the party came upon a rough shack built of tree limbs, dry grass, and brushwood. Daniel was inside, cooking his supper. Skins of animals that he had shot were scattered on the floor of the hut.

Daniel looked up at the men opposite him. "What's all the excitement?" he asked.

"Why, we thought you were lost, Dan!" exclaimed Mr. Boone. "Didn't you hear the guns go off?"

The lad had been so intent on his cooking that he had scarcely heeded the shots of the searchers. "Oh," he said, "I heard all the shooting. But I thought some hunters were after deer. You needn't have worried. I can take care of myself."

And so he could. For the rest of his life he continued to roam the forests. As the settlers came in and cut down the trees, he kept moving west. Finally he had moved far beyond the Ohio valley.

Even Daniel's last home was built in the midst of a wilderness. There he watched his sons and daughters grow up. There he spent his happiest days, hunting and trapping in the woods he had always loved.

The Spelling Bee

"Spell *porridge*," said the schoolmaster.

"*Porridge*. P-o-r-r-i-d-g-e," slowly spelled the entire class.

It was a bare, dreary country schoolroom in New England, in the year 1770. There were no wall maps, pictures, or bookshelves to make the room pleasant. There were no pictures in the schoolbooks to make learning easier. There was a fireplace in the room. But it scorched the faces of those near it and left those a few feet away shivering.

As the teacher pronounced the words, he did not see the pupils passing a note around.

From one long bench to the other went the note, and from one child to the next. Each boy and girl read the note eagerly. It was an invitation.

> Come to my house to a Spelling
> Bee and Taffy Pull Friday night at
> candle-lighting.
>
> Noah Webster

Blue eyes and brown turned toward the tall, slender boy with a high forehead and dark-red hair who had given the invitation. There was high excitement at the thought of another spelling contest and taffy pull at Noah Webster's house.

Upon their arrival Friday at the Webster home, the young guests found a half-circle of vacant chairs arranged before the fireplace. When the boys and girls took their places, the flames from the great logs shone upon happy faces. Spelling at the Websters' was a jolly party, not a tedious task.

Noah's younger sister and brother were seated with the guests. Noah stood opposite them, his back to the fire. He looked very serious.

Noah began to give out the words from a
list he had made. His gray eyes gleamed.
His square jaw was firm. Spelling to Noah
Webster was a very important matter.

The delightful odor of boiling taffy came
from a huge kettle over the fire. But the
real business of the evening had everyone's
attention.

"Color," Noah pronounced and motioned to
Rebecca Hooker. She sat in the first chair
next to Noah's sister, Jerusha.

"C-o-l-o-u-r," Rebecca answered.

"Wrong! Leave the circle," said Noah.

The other children giggled. They all knew why Noah had put Rebecca out of the circle. The schoolmaster taught them to spell in the English manner—c-o-l-o-u-r, o-d-o-u-r.

But Noah Webster was a loyal American. He believed that the better way of spelling words like *color* and *odor* was the simpler New England way—without the *u*.

Next it was Jerusha's turn to take the word *color*. "C-o-l-o-r," spelled Jerusha as she moved into Rebecca's vacant chair.

The spelling bee went on. Noah gave out words familiar to the New England people. Some of these were *stall, cupboard, rescue, pitch, soul, opossum, mischief, cousin*.

Finally only Jerusha was left. The other children did not mind. "What else could be expected," they thought, "from a girl who has Noah Webster for a brother!"

Now came the more interesting part of the evening. With a piece of black, scorched wood, Noah drew a picture of a bear on the pine walls of the kitchen. As he drew, he told a story about the picture and wrote the difficult words on the wall.

Noah's audience crowded admiringly about him. Because of the story and the picture, his pupils could easily remember the spelling of these words.

Before long Noah had almost covered the kitchen walls with pictures and words. Then the pine walls were scrubbed, but the words remained clearly in the minds of those boys and girls. It was a pleasure to learn by Noah's way of teaching.

Now the party grew noisier. Games were played. The taffy was pulled and eaten with delight.

As the Websters' tall grandfather clock was striking nine, the guests began to put on their wraps. Soon they departed, their lanterns in their hands. Walking along the dark roads, they complained about the high prices they had to pay for schoolbooks.

"I shall have no new shoes all winter," Rebecca said sadly. "That's because Father had to buy me an arithmetic and a Bible for school. Books should be cheaper."

"I reckon Noah Webster is smart enough to make a book," said Betsy Hand. "Noah knows so many words. He draws very good pictures, too."

"Noah make a book? You must be out of your wits!" William Duke exclaimed.

The others agreed. Noah Webster could draw pictures that certainly made spelling fun. But no one with any wits at all would think that Noah could write a book. What a comical idea!

But they would not have laughed if they could have seen into the future. When they grew up, their own children used a spelling book that Noah Webster had made.

The book contained lists of words used every day by American boys and girls. It also contained pictures and stories that helped pupils remember the words. When the children used this book, learning how to spell was no longer a dreary task for them.

Thousands of Webster spellers were taken by settlers to all parts of the country. The books went west, south, and north. They went in stagecoaches, covered wagons, ox-carts, puffing little steam trains, and aboard river boats.

Meanwhile, Noah Webster himself went from farms to villages, and from villages to towns, explaining his speller to the teachers. Soon he carried with him a dictionary that he had made. It, too, had pictures to help explain the meanings of words.

With his speller and his dictionary, Noah taught countless numbers of boys and girls who lived far beyond the kitchen walls of his New England home.

Fulton's Folly

It was a hot afternoon in the late spring of 1779. Young Robert Fulton was going out fishing with his friend Christopher and Christopher's father.

Robert frowned as he pushed the long pole into the creek bottom and shoved with all his strength. The boys had worked all day. Both were tired. But there was still more work to be done before they could enjoy any fishing.

Their heavy, flat-bottomed boat had to be poled a long way up the shallow stream. Besides being heavy, the boat was awkward and hard to steer.

Adapted and reprinted from *Boat Builder, the Story of Robert Fulton* by Clara Ingram Judson; copyright, 1940, by Charles Scribner's Sons; used by permission of the publishers.

"There should be an easier way to move a boat than this!" Robert said impatiently.

Christopher looked at Robert in surprise. "But we have to use either oars or a pole. We can't go upstream any other way."

"I should think an engine could be used to move a boat," Robert argued. "People use steam engines to do all kinds of work now. Why not move a boat with one?"

"Have you lost your wits?" Christopher's father cried. "The engine's weight would sink a boat. No one will ever move a boat very far with steam."

After the boys had finally poled the boat to the fishing spot, they took a swim to cool off. Afterwards they caught a good string of fish. But the idea that there should be a better way to move a boat upstream still lingered in Robert's mind.

Several weeks later Christopher's father wanted to go fishing again. But when he came to the creek bank, his boat was gone. A sound up the creek caught his attention. Coming toward him around a bend was his boat.

Something odd was fastened to each side of the boat. Robert was standing up in the center, turning a strange-shaped rod.

"They work!" Christopher called. "The paddles work!" His father was speechless. Had those boys ruined his boat?

Christopher took a pole from the bottom of the boat and steered toward the bank.

Then Robert spoke up. "I was sure that there must be a better way to move a boat. I invented a way, and Christopher helped me fix up your boat. You turn this crank to move the two paddles on the sides. Then the paddles move the boat. It's really very simple. Won't you try it, sir?"

Christopher's father looked doubtful. "No, you do it," he said, stepping into the boat.

So after Christopher had turned the boat around, Robert worked the crank. Slowly but steadily they moved upstream.

The invention was a great success. All the village boys wanted rides. They were even willing to turn the crank for a chance to go on the boat. Every evening villagers came to watch the boat sweep upstream with delighted boys cranking the paddles.

Though Robert was excited by the success of his invention, he did not forget his idea of boats run by steam. If a hand-turned crank moved a boat, he reasoned, why wouldn't a steam engine do the task even better? But for years he did nothing about his idea. He was more interested in other things.

The lad had always been skillful at drawing and painting. When he was seventeen, he began to earn his living by painting and selling pictures. Later he went abroad in a sailing ship to study art in England. For many years he remained there and became an excellent painter.

All over England and in France there was talk of steam engines and of the work they could do. People said that there was great need to move things faster by water.

Fulton's interest in a steam-run boat was renewed by this talk. Many other men had attacked the problem of building such a boat but had failed to solve it completely. Fulton felt sure he could do it. In France he met a man who helped him develop his ideas, and he actually built a steam-powered boat.

The boat was small, and there was little space for passengers. People jeered at it. But it amazed the watching crowds by running under its own power for several miles upriver and back to the dock.

Fulton was encouraged by this success. So he decided to leave France and build a steamboat in the United States. He wanted to build one that would carry passengers and cargo. In the autumn of 1806, after twenty years abroad, he sailed for New York.

Immediately upon his arrival he started to work. He arranged to have the new boat built in a New York shipyard. He ordered the engine from England.

Work on the new steamboat went swiftly. By the following spring it was well along. The engine came from England. After being carefully checked, it was put in place.

In July the boat was nearing completion. Great crowds gathered to look at it. They jeered just as the people had done earlier in France. They called the new steamboat "Fulton's Folly."

"It will never work," they said gleefully.

By the late summer of 1807 the boat was ready to be tested. Fulton invited some of his friends to make the first trip with him. The boat was to run upriver for a distance of one hundred fifty miles.

The day of the test was clear and warm. Curious throngs lined the riverbank to watch Fulton prove his folly.

"How people will laugh at us if the boat doesn't go!" said the passengers on deck.

Suddenly a bell rang, and ropes were cast off. Fulton gave the signal to start. The engine began to rumble, while all the people held their breath. Then the engine stopped. There was no sound but the lapping of the water against the boat.

On the bank the watchers began to laugh.

"Told you she wouldn't go!" they jeered. "Now look at Fulton's Folly!"

Meanwhile, all the passengers wondered if they should go ashore. Then Fulton stepped up on a deck seat and spoke loudly enough to be heard on the dock.

"Do not be annoyed by the delay, friends. Give me half an hour. I'll get us going, or we'll give up the trip for the day."

Fulton stepped down and went to examine the engine. Soon he found what the trouble was and corrected it. A few minutes later the paddle wheel began to turn, and the boat started upriver.

At first all the watchers were speechless. Then the silence ended in a shout of triumph echoing from shore to ship and back again. Men tossed hats into the air. Women waved their handkerchiefs and hugged each other with excitement. All the passengers on the boat rushed to shake Fulton's hand.

Robert Fulton was excited, too. He had proved that his steamboat would really go! Now people and cargoes could travel safely and cheaply over the lakes and rivers of the United States. And someday a steamboat would cross the ocean.

How a Song Named a Flag

In the year 1814 a large new flag waved over the fort guarding the city of Baltimore.

"It's a grand flag," said Mary Pickersgill, who had made it. "It's a strong flag, too," Mary boasted. "Those broad stripes will never tear apart. I fastened them thread by thread, to hold together forever, like our United States."

Caroline Pickersgill regarded the flag with shining eyes and echoed her mother's words. "Yes, it's a grand flag," she said. Her own skillful sewing had helped make the brilliant banner in the Pickersgill flag shop.

The huge flag was about thirty-three feet long and twenty-seven feet wide. This was the largest flag that Mary Pickersgill had ever made. It could be seen from both land and sea.

In the streets of Baltimore the citizens looked up thankfully at the huge flag waving over the fort. "As long as it waves, we'll be safe," they thought.

One day a small ship was sailing past the fort. On it was a young man who forgot all else as he admired the bright banner. How magnificent it looked against the sky!

At the sight Francis Scott Key bared his head. "A star-spangled banner!" he said to himself. Then he added a wish, "Long may it wave."

The United States was again at war with England. The nearby city of Washington had been attacked, and some Americans had been captured.

Among these prisoners was an old doctor whom everyone loved. He was being held on an enemy ship. Naturally many Americans were anxious for Dr. Beans' safety.

Francis Scott Key was sailing to rescue the prisoner. Key's ship carried a flag of truce to protect it from being fired upon by the enemy ships. But first he must find the ship on which Dr. Beans was held.

At last the English warships were found. The officer in charge of them permitted Dr. Beans to go aboard the truce ship at once. But the truce ship was forced to stay with the English fleet, which was preparing for a surprise attack on the fort that guarded Baltimore. Dr. Beans, Francis Scott Key, and another American aboard the truce ship spent a dreary week of anxious waiting.

Finally the English fleet sailed to attack, and the United States truce ship was taken along.

The truce ship was held back of the war-ships. The three Americans on deck took turns watching the battle through a powerful spyglass.

When the warships first started to bomb the fort, no guns answered from the shore. The three loyal watchers groaned. Then the enemy fleet moved up closer. Immediately the guns of the fort roared violently.

The warships moved back, badly damaged. Francis Key felt encouraged. All day long he stood on the ship's deck. His eyes were glued to the Stars and Stripes, still waving over the fort.

Before midnight the enemy renewed their attack. Again the Americans on the deck of the distant truce ship watched the firing. By the light of the bursting bombs they saw their star-spangled flag clearly.

Just before dawn the bombing ceased, and Francis Scott Key waited anxiously to see the fort. At daybreak he cried in triumph, "It's there! The flag is still there!"

In the meantime, under cover of darkness, the enemy fleet had sailed away. Now the truce ship was free to return to Baltimore. On the way Key was busy writing something on a piece of paper.

"Listen!" he cried, showing the paper to his companions. He sang the words on it to an old, familiar tune. His friends joined in and sang, too.

> 'Tis the star-spangled banner.
> Oh, long may it wave
> O'er the land of the free
> And the home of the brave.

People all over the country began singing Francis Scott Key's song. People still sing it. It is called "The Star-Spangled Banner."

A Boy and His Book

Pigeon Creek was a lonely place when the pioneers began to settle in Indiana. But as young Abraham Lincoln tramped across a field, he was thinking how much he loved his new home in the Indiana wilderness.

The Lincoln cabin was roughly built. At night from his bed in the loft, the lad could see the sky through the cracks between the logs. Great white stars shone down on him. Sometimes the yellow moon lighted his room like a bright candle. Sometimes on warm summer nights cooling raindrops fell gently over his face. In winter feathery flakes of snow fell on his pillow.

Today the sturdy youth was hurrying home with good news. A school was starting nine miles from Pigeon Creek. Abe meant to go and get some book learning.

Early the next morning Abe and his older sister Sally got ready for the long walk to school. Nancy, their mother, saw that they were neat and clean. Then she sent them off with a loving pat.

"Now go and learn all you can," she told them. And away they went. They were both dressed in clothing made entirely by their mother. She had even made Abe's coonskin cap. His boots were made from bearskin.

After a few days of school Sally tired of the daily eighteen-mile walk. She did not go any more. But young Abraham considered no distance too great if only he could learn to spell and write and to read books.

About a month later the school closed so that pupils could help with the spring planting. Abe was much disappointed. He knew, however, that the pioneer farmers of Indiana needed all the help they could get to plow their fields and to raise and harvest their crops.

Abe was big and sturdy for a boy of his age. He tried his best to do a man's work. But as he worked, he never stopped thinking about books. He never stopped wishing that he knew what they contained.

The next year a strange illness brought sorrow to the community at Pigeon Creek. The illness was so terrible that many people died. Abe's mother was one of them.

For a long time after her death the boy did not go to school. He spent all his time helping Sally with the housework or hunting and fishing.

Then one day Mr. Lincoln brought home a new wife with three children of her own.

The new wife was a good mother to Abe and Sally. She knew how much Abe wanted book learning and sent him back to school. But in the Indiana wilderness, school was open for just a few weeks during the winter season. And Abe was often absent while he helped his father chop wood or pull fodder.

In those few weeks of school the boy learned reading, writing, spelling, and some arithmetic. He liked reading best of all, but books were scarce in Pigeon Creek.

The Lincoln family owned only two books—a Bible and an arithmetic. The Bible was hard to read, and Abe often stumbled over the words. The arithmetic was easier. He studied it from cover to cover.

Abe borrowed every book anyone would lend him. He read each one until he knew it almost by heart.

One cold day he tramped five miles over rough fields to help a farmer pull cornstalks for fodder. When he came in to dinner at noon, he saw a book on a table.

"Could I borrow it?" he asked.

Abe's eyes sparkled with pleasure when he left with the book tucked under his arm. At home he swallowed his supper quickly. Then he stretched out flat on the floor with his borrowed book. He read until midnight by the light of the crackling fire.

When Abe went up to his bed in the loft, he tucked the book between two logs of the wall. At dawn, when he reached for it, his fingers touched something wet and cold.

The book was soaked with snow that had blown in through the cracks. Now it was ruined! The only honest thing he could do was to go and tell the owner. The boy did not hesitate. He set out without waiting for breakfast or combing his hair.

Abe told the farmer his sad story. "Oh, please, sir," he said anxiously, "I'll pull fodder or do anything you say to make up for spoiling your book."

"Well," drawled the farmer, "I reckon two days' work will pay for it. Pull fodder for two days and keep the book."

So Abe toiled for two days. He did not mind that his back ached and his hands were stiff with cold. The precious book was his! It was a story about George Washington.

Years afterwards Abraham Lincoln often told about the Washington book. "It helped me become President of the United States," he always said.

A Great Showman

One winter day in 1824 a lad of fourteen stood on a narrow street in a New England village. He was listening to a group of excited men. In the center of the group was a neighbor who had just returned from a visit to the world beyond the village. The man had been forty miles from home, and everyone was inquiring about his trip.

"How did you find the roads?"

"What places are there along the way to get food and rest for man and horse?"

"What do people outside our village talk about? How do they entertain themselves?"

The boy was even more curious than the others. Soon he had an opportunity to ask the question that was on his mind.

"John," he said, "didn't you see anything new or strange outside?"

"Yes, Taylor," the man replied. "I saw a dog that had two tails."

"Honestly?" asked Taylor in amazement. "That is very curious."

A thought occurred to Taylor Barnum. If only he had that dog, he could make a lot of dimes and nickels exhibiting it.

"Do you think I could buy the dog?" the youth asked eagerly.

"Why, yes," John said slowly. "I guess five or ten dollars would buy him."

"Then I'll start out in the morning to find him," Taylor declared.

"Well, see me before you go," John said. "I might think of something to help you."

The next morning Taylor mounted one of his father's sturdy horses and started off to seek the strange animal. But before he left the village, he remembered to stop to see his neighbor.

"Well, John, I'm off to find that dog," the boy said. "Have you any advice?"

"Y-yes," drawled his neighbor. "I forgot to mention that the dog with two tails was coming from behind the counter in a meat market. He carried one tail in his mouth."

The joke about the two-tailed dog became famous in the small community. But Taylor was not angry. Playing jokes was one way that the people could entertain themselves. It was their chief amusement.

The Barnum family had very little money. So Taylor, the oldest of the children, got a job working in a store. He was good at it, too. He had a witty way of talking about his goods. And because the customers were entertained, they bought things they did not really need.

As Taylor Barnum grew older, he roamed all over the country, working at many kinds of jobs. But he was always interested in collecting strange things for people to see.

Once when Barnum was working in New York City, he walked by a place where many odd animals and curious objects were being exhibited. People were paying ten cents to look at this collection. But Barnum thought that he could make the business pay much better if he owned it.

The owner was willing to sell Barnum the entire collection for twelve thousand dollars. Barnum arranged to pay for it out of his earnings.

When he took charge, only the two words *American Museum* were on the outside of the building. There was nothing else outside to attract attention to the museum or to advertise it. But that was soon changed.

One morning passers-by blinked their eyes in surprise. Immense bright-colored signs, covering the front of the museum, captured their attention. Each sign described one of the exhibits inside the building.

A band played all day. At night big gas-lights shone on the signs. Tickets cost a quarter, and people swarmed inside. There they saw wild beasts and strange birds, such as pelicans and parrots. There were freaks, too, one of which was a two-headed calf.

There were also lifelike wooden figures of famous people from all parts of the world. Almost every kind of machine that had been invented was exhibited.

The American Museum attracted sightseers from everywhere. It was the talk of New York. "What will Barnum do next?" was on everybody's tongue.

Business was so good that Barnum sent men to faraway countries to find new and freakish things for his collection. Besides odd-looking animals, there were magicians, stiltwalkers, tightrope walkers, and sword swallowers.

There were giant men and women and tiny people called midgets. One famous midget was especially small. He was less than two feet tall. Barnum named him Tom Thumb.

Tom Thumb was very quick-witted. He said many clever things and could perform clever tricks, too. He attracted so much attention in America that Barnum decided to take him abroad. The midget was exhibited to curious throngs all over the world. He was even presented to the Queen of England.

Soon Barnum became very rich. He now used his full name, Phineas Taylor Barnum.

When Phineas was about sixty years old, he started a traveling circus. This circus required a tent so large that everyone was amazed at its size. Instead of one ring for performers, the "big top" had two.

Phineas Taylor Barnum's big show became more famous than before when an enormous elephant named Jumbo joined it. By that time the big top had three rings.

Three acts all going at once! No wonder audiences swarmed to Barnum's big top!

Never had there been so large a collection of freaks. Never had one show contained so many people, so many horses, so many monkeys, giraffes, lions, tigers, and other wild animals, or so many clowns. And the people never tired of seeing Tom Thumb, the midget, and Jumbo, the huge elephant.

Phineas Taylor Barnum grew so famous that people went to his circus to see *him* as well as Tom Thumb, Jumbo, and all the freaks. Barnum was always ready to talk to people. They fondly called him "Old P. T."

Often Barnum would sit in the audience with groups of children. One of his great delights was watching their amusement.

Of course there were other circuses, too. Soon the owner of the biggest of these was persuaded to join with Barnum. Together they made the Greatest Show on Earth. It still travels over the country. And everywhere it goes, some people still talk about Jumbo, Tom Thumb, and P. T. Barnum—the greatest showman who ever lived.

Nothing for Herself

One Saturday there was big excitement at the Barton farm. The barnyard was filled with men. The whole community had come with tools and ladders to help the Bartons raise a new barn. By noon the timbers of the frame were in place, and the siding had been nailed to the lower story.

Mrs. Barton, with her three daughters, served dinner in the yard. Clara Barton, the youngest daughter, poured the milk and passed the bread.

Just as dinner was over, everyone looked up at the barn. There was David Barton climbing up the frame.

"How wonderful David is!" thought Clara. "He is so strong! He can do anything."

The lad reached the top of the frame and stepped out onto a board. As he stood on the board, it broke and David fell.

For a while no one thought that he was badly hurt. He just had a headache.

"No broken bones," announced the doctor after examining the sturdy youth. "He'll be all right."

But after a month had passed, David still had a headache. It gradually grew worse, and at last he could not get out of bed. He lay there with a high temperature.

The whole family waited on David. But Clara was the only one he wanted near him. Every night she rested on a pile of quilts beside David's bed. She hardly slept at all. Weeks went by, and David's illness became steadily worse. There were times when he did not recognize people.

Then at last he began to improve. "Why aren't you in school?" he asked Clara.

"I didn't want to go, David. I wanted to stay with you until you were well."

"That may be a long time," David replied. "The doctor doesn't come any more. Everybody thinks I'll never get well. Everyone has given me up!"

"No, David," cried Clara earnestly. "I'll never give you up!"

David moaned feebly. "I'm so tired," he sighed. "Read to me, Clara."

Slowly and softly the girl started to read from the Bible. She read until her brother fell asleep.

For over a year David had to stay in bed. The young nurse never left her patient for more than an hour or two at a time.

When David had finally recovered, Mrs. Barton began to worry about Clara.

"Now you are not so well as David," she said. "You didn't grow an inch or put on any weight all during David's illness. And you try to hide from people. You seem to be afraid of them."

"It's because I can't get used to seeing people," Clara replied. "I didn't see anyone except the family for all those months that I was David's nurse."

"You'll have to catch up with the times," Mr. Barton told Clara. "You are so far behind that I'll bet you don't even know who the President of the United States is!"

"I'll bet I do. Andy Jackson!"

"Right!" her father chuckled. "You always were a smart girl."

Soon Clara returned to school. She had excellent teachers and rapidly caught up in her studies. But she could not overcome her shyness with people whom she did not know.

"How can we help Clara have a happy future?" her mother asked a friend who was visiting the family. "Clara deserves all the good she can get out of life."

"She may always be shy," the guest said. "Probably she will never be interested in getting things for herself. Her happiness lies in helping the people who need her. For others she will fight fearlessly. Whatever she undertakes, she'll never fail."

After Clara grew up, she began to teach. She did not fail. She was very patient and kind to her young pupils, and she never gave up trying to teach them all the things they should know.

After teaching fifteen years, Clara began another task. The country was torn apart by a violent war. Clara determined to do something to help save the lives of wounded men. They required care before they were taken from the battlefields to hospitals.

It seemed an impossible task for a woman to undertake, but again Clara did not fail. She kept trying till she obtained permission to take supplies to the dreary battlefields.

Clara gave first aid to the wounded before they were moved to hospitals. To keep them from starving, she cooked food over an open fire on the battlefield.

Soon she had people to assist her. Some of them collected first-aid supplies, clothing, food, and money. They sent these things to Clara. Then other people helped give out the supplies on battlefields and in hospitals and prison camps.

When the war ended in 1865, Clara's work for her country was not over. She began a task that required the aid of the government. Clara did not hesitate. Determined to see President Abraham Lincoln, she went to the White House in Washington.

"Mr. President," Clara said earnestly, "I receive hundreds of letters from families and friends of missing soldiers. They all want to know if their men are dead or if they are in hospitals. It is just impossible for me to answer all the questions.

"The newspaper lists of dead and wounded are often wrong. The government ought to have a department to supply correct lists. People deserve to know what has become of their missing loved ones."

Clara did not speak to President Lincoln in vain. "The government will assist you in your work," he promised.

Before long, Clara obtained an office, with government workers to search for news of missing soldiers. Now at last she was able to answer all the letters she received about them, and her replies often brought comfort to saddened families. Once more Clara did not fail those who needed her help.

Even when this job was completed, Clara Barton did not stop toiling for others. She crossed the ocean and worked as a nurse in another war. This time she was with a new group known as the Red Cross. The group aided the wounded soldiers of any country that agreed to the Red Cross rules.

"If I live to return to America," Clara said, "I shall try to make the people understand the purpose of the Red Cross. I'll try to get America to join the Red Cross."

This was not an easy task. Clara had to ask the aid of three Presidents before she succeeded. At last the American Red Cross was started, with Clara Barton at its head. The shy young nurse had become the most famous and best-loved woman in America.

Night Is Turned into Day

"Mother, may I have some money?" Tom Edison asked as he came into the kitchen.

"Money!" his mother echoed in surprise. "What on earth did you do with that whole silver dollar you had last week?"

"I spent it on stuff to make a bomb," the boy replied. "Now I need more money to buy things for my inventions."

"Then you'll have to earn it," said Mrs. Edison. "But not now. Now, I want you to get me some stovewood. And you haven't filled the lamps yet. They're on the back porch. Trim the wicks, too."

"Smelly old things!" the boy muttered as he went out to the porch. He lifted the can containing coal oil and poured the smelly oil carefully into each lamp. Then he trimmed the greasy wicks and cleaned the dirty glass chimneys.

When the job was finished, he carried the lamps into the house and placed them in the rooms where they belonged.

"There!" he said, setting the last lamp on the kitchen table. "That poky job is done! I should think there'd be a better way to light houses than with oil lamps."

"In the cities they have gaslights," said his mother. "But even if we had them here in Port Huron, I know what you would say. You'd say they ought to be improved."

"Guess I would," Thomas Edison drawled calmly. "Gas can kill you if you breathe it. It's even more dangerous than these awful coal-oil lamps."

"Well, you can worry about better ways to light the Port Huron houses while you get me some stovewood!" his mother said.

"All right," the boy replied with a grin.

But while he filled the woodbox, he was not thinking about new ways to light houses. He was wondering how to earn some money. This was not easy in the little community of Port Huron. He wished he could earn enough money to obtain everything he needed for his workshop and inventions.

The boy's wish came true, but not until twenty years later. By that time Thomas Alva Edison owned one of the biggest workshops in the world. The Port Huron youth had grown rich and famous by inventing new machines. Yet he still worked day and night on other new ideas.

It was twelve o'clock one October night in the year 1879. In Edison's workshop men were still talking. Edison sat humped over a table. At last he rose from his chair.

"That's all for now, boys," he announced. "You fellows build the power plant that I've described so we can obtain more electricity. I'll continue my experimenting with the bulb. I'm going to invent a good electric light if it takes me all the rest of my life. People need bright, safe lights for their houses."

As the others departed, he seated himself again. He sat motionless, staring absently at the wall.

"I'll bet he'll sit there all night, thinking about his light bulb," said one of the men as he left. "When you consider how long he's experimented on that light, you'd think he'd be extremely discouraged."

"Not Thomas Alva Edison!" another man declared. "He never gets discouraged."

But Edison was discouraged. Nearly a year had passed since he had undertaken to make an electric light that could be used in homes. Nearly a year of hard, steady toil, and still the job seemed to be nowhere near completion!

One kind of electric light had already been invented by someone else. But that kind of light burned out quickly. It was so bright that it hurt the eyes. And it was unsafe to use indoors.

Edison's aim was to invent a more useful, cheaper light that would be safe anywhere. He had decided to use a glass bulb for his light. For months he had been searching for the right material to burn in the glass bulb. He needed something that would glow steadily when electricity went through it.

"Every material I have experimented with has blown out, burned up, or broken when we've tested it," he thought. "I might try cotton thread again. The last time we tried it, we hadn't discovered that we had to get all the air out of the bulb before we turned on the electricity."

Locking his hands behind his head, Edison began to think of a new way to use cotton thread. The dim, gray light of dawn lit up the windows before he stood up.

"I believe I've got it," he said under his breath. "It will be worth a try anyway."

Yawning and stretching, he shoved to one side the many things on his table. Then he lay down with his head on a book. He slept soundly until his men returned to work a few hours later.

With renewed hope Thomas Edison began to experiment again with cotton thread. He prepared the little pieces of thread in a new way this time.

After many tedious trials, one prepared thread was put into an airtight glass bulb. When Edison turned on the electricity to test the bulb, it glowed brightly.

"I'll bet that cotton thread won't work," said one man. "It will go to pieces like the other materials we've experimented with."

But as the minutes and hours ticked on, it glowed steadily. Edison watched closely. All night and all the next day he sat beside the bulb.

His helpers went about doing their work as usual. But they stopped often to exclaim over the wonderful light. When they found the little lamp still burning on the second day, they became so excited that they could not work at all.

Shortly after noon the new lamp burned out. Everyone glanced at the clock.

"Forty hours!" one workman shouted in triumph. "It's burned forty hours!"

"Yes, forty hours!" Edison echoed joyfully. "If I can make a lamp that will burn forty hours, I can make a lamp that will burn a week."

Two months later, on New Year's Eve, there was a great display of Thomas Alva Edison's lamps. Over three thousand people had been attracted to the brilliant sight.

Electric lights shone brightly on both sides of the street that led to Edison's workshop. Electric lights blazed from the windows of buildings and houses. The brightness of the display seemed to turn night into day!

"Electric light is safer than gas or oil or candles," people said. "Someday it will be cheaper, too. And there are no chimneys to clean or wicks to trim!"

Inside the workshop there were displays of lights being moved about on long cords. One bulb was even burning under water.

As the throngs departed, they exclaimed, "It's astonishing! Thomas Alva Edison is indeed a wizard!"

Old Tales
from Everywhere

The Four Musicians

There was once a donkey who had worked for his master faithfully many years. But now he was feeble and unfit for work. So his master had decided to put an end to the faithful animal. The donkey realized what was going to happen and ran away.

"I shall go to the city," he said. "There I can probably get work as a musician. My body may have grown feeble, but my voice is as strong as ever."

He had not gone far when he spied a dog lying by the road. The dog was panting as if he had run a long way.

"My friend, what makes you pant so?" the donkey asked.

"Ah, me!" said the dog. "My master was going to put an end to me because I am old and toothless and can no longer make myself useful in hunting. So I ran away. But how am I to gain a living now?"

"Listen!" said the donkey. "I am going to the city to be a musician. Why don't you accompany me and see what you can do in the same line of work?"

The dog wagged his tail and accepted the donkey's invitation. They went on together and soon came to a cat sitting by the road. She looked as dismal as three wet days.

"What is the matter with you, my good lady?" asked the donkey. "You look quite out of spirits."

"Ah!" said the cat. "How can I be cheerful when my life is in danger? I am getting old and feeble, and my teeth are no longer sharp enough to catch mice. So today my mistress threatened to drown me. It was my good fortune to get away from her. But I do not know what is to become of me!"

"Leave your cruel mistress," replied the donkey. "Come with us to the city and be a musician. You have always understood music. Therefore, you ought to be able to make a good living by entertaining people."

The cat liked the idea and went on with the donkey and the dog. As they passed a farmyard, a rooster flew up on the gate.

"Cock-a-doodle-doo!" he screamed.

"Splendid!" cried the donkey. "Upon my word, you make a fine noise! What is all the crowing about?"

"I was only announcing fair weather for our washing day," said the rooster. "I do that every week. But my mistress doesn't thank me for my trouble. She has told the cook that I must be made into stew for the guests who are coming tomorrow."

"You, too, have a cruel mistress," said the donkey. "Come with us, Master Chanticleer. We are going to the city to be musicians. You possess a good voice. If all of us sing tunes together, we should have no trouble finding an audience. So come along."

It was more than a day's journey to the city. The four animals decided, therefore, to spend the night in the woods. The dog and the donkey lay down under an oak tree. The cat climbed up in the branches. And the rooster flew up to the very top.

Before the rooster went to sleep, he looked around to see that everything was all right. In so doing, he saw a little light shining in the distance.

"There must be a house not far off," he called to his companions. "I see a light."

"Then let us go there," said the donkey. "I am not used to sleeping in a forest. The sooner we find a better place, the happier I shall be."

"Yes," said the dog. "And we are hungry and thirsty, without even a crust of bread. Perhaps we shall find some food there."

The cat and the rooster came down from the tree, and they all paraded toward the house, with Chanticleer in the lead.

When they reached the house, the donkey, being the tallest, looked in the window.

"Well, what do you see?" asked the dog.

"I see that the house belongs to thieves," said the donkey. "Swords and guns are on the walls, and chests of money on the floor. The thieves are all sitting at a table that is loaded with good things to eat and drink."

"Those things to eat and drink would just suit us," declared the rooster.

"Indeed they would," replied the donkey. "But we cannot get at them unless we first manage to drive the thieves away."

The animals soon hit upon a plan. The donkey stood with his forefeet on the window ledge. The dog climbed on the donkey's back. The cat jumped up on the dog's back. And the rooster perched on the shoulders of the cat. Then they began their music.

"Heee-eee-aw!" squawked the donkey.

"Bow-wow!" barked the dog.

"Meow! Meow!" cried the cat

"Cock-a-doodle-doo!" crowed the rooster.

At the completion of their song, they burst through the window. The thieves, thinking an ugly troll was about to attack them, fled in panic.

At once the animals proceeded to eat the good food. Then they put out the light, and each found a sleeping place to his liking.

The donkey lay down in the yard. The dog stretched out inside the house by the door. The cat curled up on the hearth. And the cock flew up and slept on the chimney.

About midnight the thieves came sneaking back toward the house. All was quiet.

"I think we ran away without reason," the thieves' captain said. "But let us take no risks. You stay outside while I see if we are likely to have any more trouble."

He entered the kitchen quietly. The cat was now awake, watching with shining eyes.

The thief thought the cat's eyes were two live coals. He reached down to get a light by touching a match to them. Now the cat did not enjoy that sort of thing. She sprang into the thief's face, scratching wildly.

He cried out in terror and ran toward the door. There the dog bit him in the leg.

But the man managed to get out into the yard. At once the donkey knocked him down with a kick. Then the rooster, awakened by the noise, cried out, "Cock-a-doodle-doo! Cock-a-doodle-doo!"

Crawling away to the other thieves, the captain said, "We cannot live in that house any more. In the kitchen a horrible witch scratched me with her sharp nails. By the door a man pierced my leg with a knife. In the yard a tar-black giant beat me with a stick. And on the roof a fellow kept shouting, "Toss him up to me!"

So the thieves went away and never came back. The four musicians were so pleased with their new quarters that they did not go to the city. They stayed where they were. And they may be there to this very day.

A Barber's Discovery

Once there lived in a village a very fine barber named Garo. As he served his customers, Garo was always glad to give them advice. And as long as there was hair to cut or a beard to trim, he never ran out of things to say.

In those days a barber traveled from house to house, like a peddler, to do his work. So old Garo had a chance to observe just what was occurring. For this reason his advice was considered excellent.

Because Garo gave so much advice, people thought that he was very wise indeed. And you may be sure that Garo himself agreed with them. He felt that he had no equal.

One November afternoon Garo was resting beneath a great oak tree. His head leaned comfortably against the bark as he gazed at a nearby field. There pumpkins lay yellow and fat in the sunshine. Garo observed how the fat pumpkins clung to slender vines that wandered here and there like pieces of lost string.

Yawning sleepily, the barber happened to glance upward. From the branches of the oak tree hung hundreds of tiny brown acorns. They were ready to fall at the first harsh blast of winter wind.

Suddenly Garo wrinkled up his forehead. Then he squinted his eyes and stroked his beard. He always did these things when he had made a discovery.

"Lo and behold!" he exclaimed. "Nature has made a big mistake! Observe these tiny acorns. They hang on branches that are sturdy enough to bear the weight of an ox.

But big pumpkins grow on stringlike vines. How foolish! Even a simpleton knows that heavy pumpkins should grow on sturdy oaks and dainty acorns on slender vines."

Old Garo lay there, stroking his beard and squinting. How his customers would marvel when he told them of his discovery! "It's a pity I wasn't around when the world began," he said to himself. "I could have provided Nature with good advice." And so saying, the barber folded his hands over his fat stomach and fell into a deep slumber.

His stomach under his yellow shirt looked a great deal like one of those huge pumpkins. And his puffy brown nose did not look very different from one of the acorns on the oak branches above his head.

Garo began to snore loudly, just as he always did when he slumbered. As he snored, he smiled. He was dreaming of his wonderful discovery.

All of a sudden an acorn was loosened by the wind. Down it fell from a high branch. It landed on Garo's nose with a loud plop, right in the middle of a snore.

The startled barber's snore turned to an angry snort. Then he caught a glimpse of the acorn that had plopped down on his nose, making it red and sore. Gently rubbing his nose with his fingers, he stared at the acorn thoughtfully.

Finally, still rubbing his sore nose, Garo said meekly, "How foolish I was even to consider giving advice to Nature! And how sore my nose would be if that acorn had been a pumpkin! Nature always knows best what is good for the world."

With that wise and solemn remark, he set out for home.

Tyll's Masterpiece

This is a tale about merry Tyll, who lived by his wits. His chief interest was helping people recognize their follies so that they would act more wisely in the future. To do this, he often played tricks upon people.

One day he was riding his donkey along a lonely road. Suddenly the beast stopped.

Tyll got down and pulled at the reins with might and main, but the donkey refused to move. So Tyll stripped some branches from a berry bush and mounted the donkey again. Then he stretched out his arm and held the branches before the animal's mouth.

The donkey, seeing food so close, began to amble after it. In this way Tyll coaxed the beast on until they came to the marble castle of a nobleman.

The nobleman happened to see Tyll riding along in this strange manner.

"Fellow with the merry face and strange ways," the great man called to Tyll, "what work do you do?"

"Noble lord," Tyll replied humbly, "I am a portrait painter."

"Oho!" cried the nobleman. "I am looking for just such a person. Would you like to be my court painter?"

"Gladly, my lord," said Tyll. "But if I am to live at your court, I must be as well fed and as well dressed as the other members."

"That is fair enough," said the nobleman. "Come with me."

Soon Tyll found himself dressed in robes of fine material. Then he was served at a table loaded with plates of rich food.

After dinner the nobleman said, "I want you to paint portraits of me, my wife, and all the members of my court."

"My lord," Tyll answered humbly, "your desire is my command. I will undertake to paint such portraits for two hundred gold coins."

The next morning Tyll asked that all the people whom he was to paint should pass separately before him.

First came a fat duke. "You must paint me without my fat, as I looked when I was young. Or else," the duke hissed, "I shall have you punished!"

Next came an old lady in waiting, thin and ugly. "Master painter," she threatened, "if your painting of me is not beautiful, you will find yourself in prison."

Then a young lady in waiting came along. She had yellow hair and fresh pink cheeks. But two of her front teeth were gone.

"Master," she said, "you must paint me
smiling, with no teeth missing. If you don't,
I shall have you put to death."

And so it went. Each and every member
of the court who passed Tyll threatened him
harshly. At the end of the line came the
noble lord himself.

"Tyll," he said, "I am paying you well for
these portraits. See to it, therefore, that
each is a perfect likeness of its owner. If
not, you will receive a dreadful punishment.
I will accept no excuses."

Then he departed. Left alone, Tyll began
to feel extremely worried.

"Surely no man was ever given such a difficult task," Tyll thought in distress. "I must paint each person as he wishes to look. Yet each portrait must be a perfect likeness. If I fail, I'll be imprisoned or put to death. And I thought the life of a painter was a merry one!"

Tyll thought and thought until at last he found a way out of his troubles.

"Ho, my fine ladies and gentlemen!" he cried. "I shall treat you to such portraits as were never painted before!"

Immediately he asked the nobleman for a big room with large blank walls. He also demanded that long curtains be hung over the walls from ceiling to floor. And finally he asked for three painters to assist him.

He was given the room, the curtains, and the three helpers. Then Tyll and his fellows locked themselves in, refusing to see anyone while they worked.

For thirty days the four painters lived in the room in great comfort. They were served the finest foods that the castle cooks could prepare.

On the thirty-first day the nobleman stuck his nose in the door.

"Ho, there, Tyll!" he said. "How is the painting coming along?"

"Fine, noble lord," Tyll replied.

"May I see it?"

"Not yet, my lord," Tyll answered.

After forty days the nobleman peeped in again.

"Ho, there, Tyll!" he shouted. "Is today the day?"

"My lord, the painting is almost finished," said Tyll. "But no one may enter yet."

After fifty days the noble lord became enraged. He walked right in and found the curtains drawn over the walls.

"This is nonsense!" he boomed. "Show me the painting this very instant!"

"Certainly, my lord," Tyll replied meekly. "But first you must call together here all the noble ladies and gentlemen whom I have painted."

The nobleman did so. Presently all the members of his court had gathered before the drawn curtains.

"Most noble lord," Tyll announced, "you are all about to see a brilliant masterpiece. Here are perfect likenesses painted in magic colors. I learned the great secret of these colors from a famous magician. They can be seen only by those of noble birth. But if there are common people here, they will see only a blank wall."

Then Tyll drew the curtains apart. The people stood speechless, their eyes opened wide. All they saw was a white, blank wall.

Tyll pretended to point out people on the blank wall, describing their faces and their clothes. No one dared to disagree with him. Each was afraid to say that he saw nothing.

Suddenly the Court Fool cried out, "You may call me a common fellow. I don't mind a bit. But I see only a white, blank wall."

After a brief silence Tyll burst out laughing. "When a fool is honest and tells the truth, it's time for wise men to listen. I confess that I have fooled you. But it was the only way I could please you."

With a shamefaced smile, the master of the castle spoke. "You are a clever fellow, Tyll. All of us told you how to paint our portraits. You showed us our folly.

"Here is your money. Now leave before some of my people forget the lesson they have learned and decide to punish you."

Tyll went quickly. When he was a good distance from the castle, he spoke to his donkey. "My friend, listen and learn. The secret of life is laughter. Fifty men were ready to kill me, but I laughed them out of it. Laughter makes life easy and gay."

Chanticleer and the Fox

Once upon a time a poor woman lived in a small cottage near a wood. She had little enough to eat. But she considered herself extremely fortunate to have a cow, a pig, and a few chickens.

Among her chickens was a very handsome rooster named Chanticleer. As he strutted about the barnyard, his comb looked as red as fire. His glossy feathers were as yellow as gold. For loud crowing he had no equal in all the neighborhood. And if there ever could be a King of Roosters, Chanticleer was certainly that king.

One night Chanticleer was perched by his wife in the chicken house. Suddenly he began to moan and mumble in his sleep. Then he groaned as though in great distress. He made such a fuss that his wife woke from her slumber. Looking at him with concern, she cried, "Chanticleer! What is wrong?"

Her cries woke Chanticleer. The rooster gave a start and flapped his wings loudly.

"Oh, my dear!" he exclaimed, his comb stiff with terror. "I've had a most horrible dream. You simply cannot imagine how it frightened me!"

In a shaking voice he continued, "I was in the yard, looking for worms or crickets. All at once I beheld a strange beast lurking there. He looked like a dog, but his manner was extremely fierce. He was yellowish-red in color, and he had a long, plumy tail and a pointed snout. His eyes glowed like coals of fire, and his dismal howls were terrible to hear."

"Simpleton!" said Chanticleer's wife in a scornful voice. "Why make a fuss about a ridiculous dream? Everybody knows that dreams are caused by eating too much rich food. Really you are sillier than a goose."

Such talk hurt Chanticleer's pride. So he began to relate all the dreams he had ever heard of that had come true. He was trying to prove to his wife that dreams often warned of future happenings. But she would not listen to him.

"Not *your* dreams," she said scornfully. "Quit fussing and go back to sleep."

"Yes, my dear," said Chanticleer meekly, for he was too weary to keep on arguing. So they slumbered peacefully until morning.

At the first streak of light, Chanticleer was fully awake. He flew down from his perch and strutted out to the barnyard in a royal manner. Flapping his wings, he hopped up to his usual perch on the fence. Then he started to crow.

"Cock-a-doodle-doo! Cock-a-doodle-doo!
Time for work and breakfast, too."

All the hens came down from their perches. Cackling loudly, they began to look for juicy insects. Chanticleer puffed up with pride as he saw how they scurried to obey him. He strutted up and down in the barnyard, his comb standing up like a king's crown. Whenever he ate an insect, he crowed loudly. He wanted to remind the hens that his alert eye was upon them.

The rays of the sun grew hotter and hotter. Chanticleer decided he would stop looking for insects and take a dust bath. Hastily swallowing one last cricket, he went down to the end of the fence. Here the dirt was as loose as ashes. It was cool and dry and especially good to wallow in.

While Chanticleer was wallowing in the dust, a strange beast came sneaking through the gate. It had yellowish-red fur, a long, pointed snout, and a plumy tail.

Now Chanticleer did not know it, but this was a sly old fox. He had been lurking in the bushes all morning, waiting for just this opportunity to catch Chanticleer alone.

"Good morning, Mr. Chanticleer," said the crafty fox as he regarded the rooster with watchful eyes.

When Chanticleer beheld the horrible beast of his dreams, he started up in terror. But the fox spoke again before Chanticleer had recovered from his fright.

"Don't be afraid of me," coaxed the fox in a persuading tone. "I just want a chance to win your friendship. Why, I came here this morning for that very reason. I knew both your father and mother well. I've even entertained them for dinner in my home."

The fox laughed to himself as he made this remark. He remembered with satisfaction what had occurred at that dinner. Chanticleer's parents had made him a tasty meal. He was sure their plump son would satisfy his appetite equally well.

"Your father had the finest voice I ever heard," the fox went on. "He used to stand on tiptoe, stretch out his neck, and crow with his eyes shut. I'm sure your voice equals your father's. Please, dear Mr. Chanticleer, display your friendship by letting me hear you crow."

The vain bird was much flattered. Acting on the suggestion of the crafty fox, he rose from the dust-wallow. Then he hopped up on the fence, stretched out his neck, shut his eyes, and began to crow.

Of course this was just the opportunity that the fox wanted. Before Chanticleer had finished crowing, the fox jumped up into the air and grabbed the cock by the neck. Then he flung Chanticleer over his shoulder and made off toward the woods at a great rate of speed.

The hens saw the fleeing fox and began to cackle their loudest. The old woman came running from her house to see what all the cackling was about.

"Alas! Alack!" she cried in distress. "A fox has caught Chanticleer. Help! Help!"

Down the road ran the old woman, shriek-
ing in alarm. The farmers dropped their
rakes and hoes and came to join the chase.
A cow and her calf, three hogs, two sheep,
and a black dog accompanied them, mooing
and grunting and bleating and barking.

Wasps and other insects swarmed overhead,
buzzing angrily. Even the crows stopped eating the corn and began cawing harshly. But
it was in vain. The fox kept well ahead of
them all.

Then to confuse his pursuers, he ran into
a flock of geese. The terrified fowls ran
hither and thither, hissing and squawking.

Poor Chanticleer looked around for an
opportunity to escape. Suddenly a brilliant
idea came to him. Peering around the fox's
snout, he said meekly, "Those silly, confused
people will never catch up with you at this
rate. No creature runs as fast as a fox.
They should know better than to pursue you.
Why don't you tell them to stop?"

The old fox was flattered by Chanticleer's
praise. He acted on the suggestion at once.
"Stop!" he shouted at his pursuers.

The minute the fox opened his mouth, the rooster flapped his wings wildly, flew up on the limb of a tree, and crowed:

"Cock-a-doodle-doo! Cock-a-doodle-doo!
I know how to flatter, too!"

Then the fox realized he had been fooled by his own trick. From his pointed snout to the tip of his tail he was a picture of shame. Chanticleer went home in triumph, but he promised himself never again to crow with his eyes shut or to be fooled by sly flattery.

The Seven Dancing Stars

A long, long time ago, when the world was young, a tribe of Indians dwelt in the midst of a forest. One day all the wild creatures disappeared from the forest as if by magic. Not even the most skillful hunter could bring home meat for the cooking-pots.

The tribe roamed far and wide, seeking new hunting grounds. But wherever they went, the animals vanished.

At last Chief Big Hawk called his tribe together. Briefly he related what the Great Spirit had made known to him.

"The Great Spirit will lead us toward the setting sun," Big Hawk said. "Far beyond towering cliffs is a lake, the home of many beavers. There we shall find fish that leap into nets as eagerly as bees seek blossoms. Bear and deer grow fat in the forest. Our cooking-pots will never be empty."

So once more the squaws gathered together their few belongings. At daybreak the tribe set out for the new hunting grounds.

At last they reached the lake where the Great Spirit had led them. On the shore Big Hawk stopped and raised his right hand.

"Let us all give thanks," he said earnestly. "Thank the Great Spirit for aiding us on our journey. May He be with us as we build our wigwams. May He give us good hunting and years of peace."

The Great Spirit was kind to the Indians, and they dwelt peacefully in their wigwams beside the lake. Meat was plentiful. Even an old squaw would not have returned from the woods empty-handed.

As the weather grew colder, the squaws of the tribe were busy preparing food for the coming winter. So the children were often left to find their own amusement.

One day Little Eagle, Big Hawk's eldest son, went with his seven brothers deep into the forest. There they came upon an open circle where the ground was as level as if it had been tramped upon by a thousand feet. The children gave no thought to how such an open place happened to be in the midst of a thick forest. They began a joyous dance.

Day after day they returned to dance in the mysterious circle, telling no one about it. One day as they danced, they heard a voice.

"Beware! Beware!" it called. "Strange things happen in this enchanted place."

Turning quickly, the children saw a tall, stern-looking figure. The stranger wore a robe of white feathers, and his long white hair shone like silver. "Leave this place," he warned the children solemnly. "Remember my words and never return."

The happy children paid no heed to the stranger's solemn warning. Instead, they went merrily on with their dance.

"Let us bring food tomorrow," suggested Little Eagle, who was always ready to eat. "Then we can feast as well as dance."

His seven brothers agreed. But when they asked their mother for the food, she seemed vexed and refused to prepare it. "Eat in the wigwam as you should," she said.

The brothers had to do without their feast, but they returned to the circle to dance as before. At the completion of their dance a strange thing happened. The startled children found themselves rising into the air—up, up.

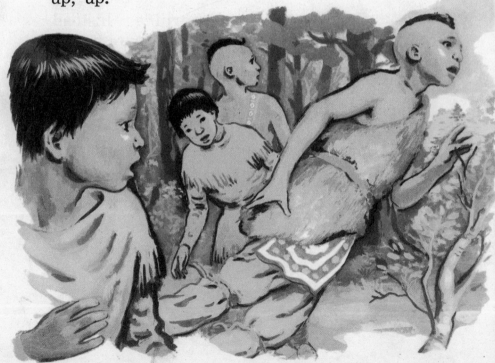

As they soared over the wigwams, their mother saw them. The squaw pleaded with them to come back. She promised them any food they desired.

Hearing his mother's words, Little Eagle glanced toward the earth. Instantly there was a blinding flash. Little Eagle had been turned into a falling star! Down to earth he plunged in a streak of light.

But his seven brothers did not look back. They all reached the sky and became stars. There they shine and twinkle to this day, a band of seven dancing stars.

Rumpelstiltskin

A Spinner of Gold

There was once a poor miller who had a beautiful daughter. He loved her dearly and was so proud of her that he could not help boasting about her.

One day a stranger came to the mill with a sack of corn to be ground into meal. He saw the dainty lass in the doorway. As he beheld her lovely face, he remarked, "I wish I had a daughter as beautiful as she."

The miller rubbed his mealy hands together and glanced at his daughter standing in the sunshine. He observed how the sun's rays, shining on her yellow hair, framed her head with golden light. He began to boast again.

"Yes, I consider her a lass in a thousand. She can spin straw into gold."

The stranger marveled at this news. He spread the tale far and wide, and soon it reached the ears of the king. Immediately the astonished king sent for the miller, telling him to fetch his daughter to the palace with him. So the miller obeyed.

"I have heard," said the king, "that this maiden can spin straw into gold. She must show if this be true. If she fails, beware, for you shall be punished."

The miller's tongue stuck in his throat, and he almost choked with fear. He dared not tell the truth about his careless boast.

The king led the dainty lass into a stable. There a spinning wheel and many bundles of straw had been placed. He looked at her and smiled. "You have straw enough here," he said. "Spin it into gold before morning."

Then he barred the door and departed.

The lass looked at the spinning wheel, and she looked at the straw. Then she thought of the punishment her father would receive the next day. Sinking down on a bench, she started to weep. In the midst of her sobs she heard a slight rustle. From underneath the straw popped a tiny man with a pointed hat on his head. He had a brown, withered face, a long red nose, and a rusty-red beard that swept down below his belt.

He regarded the maiden with piercing eyes. "Why all this fuss?" he asked harshly.

The miller's daughter was so surprised at the sight of this mere wisp of a man that she stopped crying and told him the truth.

"Pooh!" jeered the dwarf. "Spin straw into gold? That's no trouble. How will you repay me if I spin it?"

The maid had never before seen so odd and ugly a man. But his little needle-sharp eyes had such cunning that she half suspected he could do what he said. So she promised to give him her necklace.

With that, the tiny dwarf whirled dizzily on his toes. Then sitting down on a stool by the spinning wheel, he began to spin.

Whrr, whrrr, whrrr! The straw seemed to swish through the air as if caught up in a high wind. In a moment, behold! All the straw was spun into shining gold thread.

Then the long-nosed dwarf rose from his stool. Accepting the necklace, he poked it into a leather pouch, and off he went.

The next morning when the king saw all the golden thread, he was extremely pleased. But his greed increased with every glance at the shining heap.

"Well and fair," said he. "Well and fair. You shall have another trial."

Then once more he led the poor lass to a stable. This one was half-filled with straw.

"When that is spun into gold," said the king, "you shall have praise indeed. If you fail, beware of terrible punishment."

Though the king really pitied the girl, his greedy heart did not melt. He said nothing more. Turning on his heel, he went out of the stable and barred the door.

The poor maid was now greatly distressed. Yesterday's straw had been only a handful compared with today's. "Oh, if only that long-nosed dwarf were here to assist me!" she moaned.

Sadly she sat down at the wheel and tried to spin. But the straw remained only straw. "Alas and alack! There is no hope for me," she thought. But lo! To her great relief the withered dwarf appeared once more.

"Ah!" said he. "What's wrong now?"

When she told him, he combed his rusty-red beard with his bony fingers. Then he asked, "What shall I have as a reward this time if I spin for you?" She promised him the pearl ring on her finger.

He flung his beard over his shoulder and snapped his fingers. Then he plopped himself down on the stool and began to spin.

Whrrr, whrrr, whrrr went the wheel as the straw turned into golden thread. And smaller and smaller grew the heap of straw. Before dawn it was all spun, and the dwarf had vanished before the king's arrival.

The king marveled at the sight. But even yet his greedy mind was not satisfied.

"Well and fair," he said. "Only one more trial, my dear, and you shall toil no more."

This time the stable was heaped to its roof with straw.

"Spin that into gold," said the king, "and tomorrow you shall be queen."

With a glance over his shoulder he went out, barred the door, and left her to herself.

The maid sat down and looked hopelessly at the immense heap of straw. "Ah, me!" she sighed. "To spin all that into gold would require the efforts of a hundred little men."

"What, what, what!" cried a voice. In an instant little Master Long-Nose appeared for the third time.

But this time the poor trembling lass had nothing left to offer the dwarf for his work. He stared at her in silence for a moment. Then he said, "Promise me your first child if you ever have one, and tomorrow you shall be queen."

The maiden could not help being amused at such an idea. She did not suspect that she would ever be queen. So she solemnly gave the promise required of her.

The sly dwarf raised himself on his toes and whirled around nine times. After that he sat down at the wheel, whistling a tune.

Whrr, whrr, whrrr went the wheel like a swarm of bees buzzing about a hive. All night long the dwarf sat busily spinning the straw. By sunrise the heaps of straw had disappeared. They had all been spun into gold. Then the ugly little man skipped away on his wispy legs.

The king kept his promise and made the miller's daughter his queen. So she lived happily and in great comfort at the king's fine palace. When her first child was born, the young queen's joy was beyond compare.

A New Bargain

Some time after the birth of her child, the joyous life of the queen was changed. One day she knelt in the apple orchard, playing happily with her baby daughter. All at once her happiness turned to fear. Behold, there beside her was the dwarf! It seemed as if he had sprung from the trunk of a crooked apple tree nearby.

The dwarf slyly regarded the baby. "Ah! A pretty thing," he said. "And mine!"

Until now the poor queen had forgotten the promise she had made in her desperate trouble. She began to plead earnestly with the dwarf. "I will grant you anything else you ask. Only free me from my promise and let me keep my darling child."

"Nay, nay!" he refused. "A princess is a princess, and a promise is a promise. But I'll make another bargain with you. You shall have three days and nine chances to guess my name. If you have not guessed it by noon of the third day, the child shall be mine." And he disappeared as mysteriously as he had come.

All night long the queen lay wide-awake, wondering what name the ugly dwarf could possess. The next morning she went sadly to the orchard. Exactly at noon the dwarf appeared.

"Ah, Madam!" said he. "Now what's my name?" And the queen guessed the silliest names she could think of—Bumpetyboomery, Catalawampus.

But at each one the dwarf shook his head. The queen thought for a moment. Then she said a third name that popped into her mind, "Nickerruckerrubblegrubb."

The dwarf broke into a hoot of laughter. "Madam, that is not my name," he squeaked. And off he went.

Promptly at noon the next day the dwarf appeared. This time the queen guessed the three queerest names she could think of— Long-Nose, Little-Body, and Lean-Legs.

At each name the little man jiggled about, clapping his hands with glee.

"Nay, nay, Madam," he cried. "One more day, three more guesses, and the child will be mine."

On returning to the palace, the queen sent for a messenger who was sharp of hearing and as keen of eye as a hawk. She told him what the little dwarf looked like, with his withered face, wispy legs, long nose, rusty beard, and pointed hat. Then she ordered the messenger to ride like the wind, hither and thither, in search of the dwarf, and to find out his name.

"Learn his name," she said, "and immense wealth shall be yours. If you fail, you may expect to be punished harshly."

The messenger lingered not even a moment. He flung himself into the saddle and raced away on his fleet-footed steed. All night he rode hither and thither. At last, just before daybreak, he found himself at a crossroads. There he stopped and looked about.

Just beyond the crossroads the messenger could see a tiny hut. A fire burned before it. Dancing around the fire was an ugly elf. He had a withered face, wispy legs, a long nose, and a rusty-red beard flowing down below his belt.

One glimpse of the ugly, troll-like man convinced the messenger that this was the very dwarf whom the queen had sent him to find. He dismounted and crept near the fire.

The dwarf was singing a joyous tune as he danced by the firelight.

"Today I build a fire and bake.
  Tomorrow the queen's child I'll take.
  No other one is called the same,
  For Rumpelstiltskin is my name."

The messenger, lurking behind a big tree, listened carefully. He wanted to be certain of the dwarf's long name.

Then, delighted beyond measure, he crept silently back to his horse. He had barely sprung to his saddle when his steed lunged forward. Speedily the messenger galloped off to tell his news to the queen.

The queen was seated on her throne when the messenger arrived. He knelt at her feet and related to her what he had seen. After that he whispered the name he had heard.

The queen was almost overcome with joy. Immediately she dressed in her finest satin robe and velvet cloak. She even wore her most beautiful jewels. Then she went to the orchard to wait for the ugly dwarf. The royal nurse carried the baby princess, as if the child were to be given to the dwarf.

At the stroke of noon the horrible little man appeared. As usual, he had popped out from behind the mossy old apple tree. This time he wore a plume in his hat. Over his arm was a dainty shawl he had fetched to wrap about the baby.

"Ah, Madam!" cried the dwarf. "Three more guesses and the baby is mine!"

Again the queen pleaded with him. She promised him any treasure except her child. But the enraged dwarf would not listen to her. He shouted violently:

"A bargain's a bargain. A vow's a vow
    To the last word of it. Answer me now."

Smiling to herself, the queen first guessed, "Wheat-Straw."

The dwarf laughed in scornful amusement. Next she guessed, "Heaps of Gold."

The dwarf laughed louder. And then the queen smiled gleefully. She motioned for the withered dwarf to come closer. "How about Rumpelstiltskin?" she murmured.

The dwarf stared at her a moment, as if all in a wink he had been turned to stone. Then he trembled with rage and disappointment. "I vow the witches have told you my name!" he screamed.

He stamped on the ground so hard that one thin leg pierced the earth and sank into it up to the knee. Try as he might, he could not draw it out. In his fury Rumpelstiltskin grasped his other leg, trying to pull himself free. He jerked with such force that he nearly tore himself in two. But he never was able to pull himself out.

The Ugly Duckling

Mother Duck's Queer Baby

It was midsummer. The soft air was filled
with the odor of clover blossoms and other
flowers that grew in a meadow. In the midst
of the meadow was a deep, blue lake.

Among some slender reeds near the water's
edge a duck was sitting on her nest. Her
eggs were just beginning to crack open.

"Cheep! Cheep! Cheep! Cheep!" One
after another the ducklings came to life and
began to poke out their heads.

"Quack! Quack!" replied their admiring
mother. Soon the ducklings tried to quack,
too, as they ran hither and thither.

All around them lay the beautiful green world. Their mother let them look as much as they liked because green is good for the eyes. "How big the world is!" they said.

"Don't think this is the whole world," the mother duck told them. "It stretches a long, long way beyond this farm. Though I must say I've never been to the end of it myself.

"I hope you are all here," she continued. Then she lifted herself off the nest to see if all the eggs had hatched. But the biggest one had not hatched yet.

"Well, well," sighed Mother Duck. "I've never known an egg to take so long." And she settled herself on the nest again.

"How are you getting along?" called an old duck who had come for a friendly chat.

"This last egg is taking such a long time!" replied Mother Duck. "The shell will not crack open."

"Let me see the egg that will not hatch," said the old duck. "It may be a turkey's egg. The farmer's wife put one in my nest once. What trouble I had when it hatched! The creature was afraid to go near the water.

"Yes, that's a turkey's egg," she added as Mother Duck rose up from the nest. "Leave it alone. You should be teaching the ducklings to swim."

"Oh, I'll be patient and sit on it a little longer," replied Mother Duck.

"Well, I won't argue with you," said the old duck, waddling away. "I gave my advice only because of our long friendship."

At last the big egg cracked. "Cheep!" said the young one as he tumbled out of the shell. How big and ugly he was!

"What a huge duckling!" said his mother. "None of the others looked like that. Can he possibly be a turkey? Well, we shall soon find out. Into the water he shall go, even if I have to push him into it myself."

The next day was gloriously fine, and the mother duck took her family to swim.

Splash! Into the water she plopped.

"Quack, quack," she called loudly; and one after another the ducklings jumped in. The water went over their heads, but they came up to the surface again and floated properly. Their legs seemed to go of themselves quite naturally, and there they were, swimming about. Even the ugly gray one had sprung in eagerly and was swimming as well as the rest.

"Well, that is no turkey, at any rate," said Mother Duck in relief. "How well he uses his legs! How smoothly he glides along! He is my own child after all."

Then she called to the ducklings, "Come with me. I will take you into the world and introduce you to the duck yard. Keep close to me and beware of the cat."

Off she started, giving advice to the ducklings trailing along behind her.

"Remember to quack properly," said she. "Don't turn your toes in! Well-behaved ducklings turn their toes out, just as I do. Now bend your necks and say 'Quack!'"

At the duck yard the ducklings all did as they were told. But when the other fowls saw the ugly one, they hissed at him.

"Ugh, ugh!" they said. "What a frightful object he is!" Then a drake rushed at the poor creature and bit him in the neck.

"Let him alone," said the mother. "He's not bothering you."

"I know," said the drake. "But he is so ugly. It's a pity he can't be made over."

"His looks will improve as he grows older," said his mother. "He was in the egg too long. That's why he isn't properly shaped."

But his looks did not improve, and he had a miserable time. The ducks pecked him till he was sore all over. Even his brothers and sisters found fault with him.

Finally the poor creature could endure it
no longer. At the first opportunity he went
through a hedge and escaped from them all.

The Search for a Home and Friends

The ugly duckling wandered about till he
came to a hut near the edge of a swamp. It
was November now, and the wind whistled
fiercely around the poor, ugly bird. He saw
that the door was half open, and he ventured
inside without permission.

An old woman dwelt there with her cat and
her hen. "Meow," said the cat in a scornful
manner. "What do you want?"

"Just a place for shelter from the wind's
cold blasts," said the duckling humbly.

"Can you lay eggs?" demanded the hen.

"No, I can't lay eggs."

"Can you purr?" asked the cat.

"No, I can't purr," replied
the duckling.

"Well, if you can't lay eggs or purr, what can you do?" inquired the hen. She was convinced that the duckling was hopelessly stupid.

"I can swim and dive," said the duckling.

"Swim and dive!" exclaimed the cat and the hen in amusement. "Who cares to swim and dive? This is not the proper place for anyone who cannot lay eggs or purr. Go away, you useless creature!"

So the duckling departed and stayed in the reeds near a lake where the wild ducks lived. But he was so ugly that he frightened them away. After that he was always alone.

Winter set in. Dead leaves filled the air, and icy blasts howled. Dark clouds, heavy with snow, coasted across the sky.

One dismal day some enormous birds rose out of the reeds. They were swans.

The ugly duckling had never seen anything like these big birds before. They were all dazzling white with long, gracefully curved necks. Uttering strange cries, they spread their wings and circled in the air above the lake. They were preparing to fly southward, away from the region of ice and snow.

As the swans circled overhead, the duckling glided around and around in the water to watch them. Suddenly a curious sadness came over him. Then he uttered a cry so loud and strange that it frightened him.

The dismal winter days soon grew bitterly cold, and the duckling had to keep swimming to prevent the water from freezing around him. He paddled faster and faster, but at last he was so tired that he stopped moving. Soon he was a prisoner in solid ice.

Early the next morning a farmer found the helpless duckling. The man broke the ice and carried the bird home. There in the big warm kitchen the duckling began to stir about. The children made a fuss over him and tried to pet him. But the duckling was afraid and sought to escape from them.

Plop! He landed right in the milk pail, spilling milk over the floor. Next he upset the butter. Then he dived into the flour.

The two children pursued him, laughing and shouting. Their mother shrieked and slashed at him with the broom. Finally the confused bird managed to get out the door and creep off. For the rest of the winter he lurked in the midst of a swamp, without the friendship of any living creature.

In the spring when the sun had begun to shine warmly, the ugly duckling again found himself by a lake. Robins and wrens were singing joyously. Bright butterflies danced in the air.

The dazzling sunshine filled the duckling with joy. He spread his wings wide. They had grown stronger now, and to his surprise they carried him up into the air.

Up, up the bird soared. Before long he was flying over a shining pool surrounded by flowering bushes and peach and pear trees in full blossom. The odor of flowers filled the air with a glorious sweetness.

Suddenly from under the flowering bushes three dazzling white swans came swimming. They floated along as lightly as butterflies. When the duckling recognized them, the same sadness came over him. He felt he had no choice but to go to them, even though they might peck him to death.

Down he flew and swam toward the three swans. They glided out to meet him, their white feathers gleaming. The poor duckling bowed his head. He was ready to endure any punishment, however harsh it might be.

Then he saw himself mirrored in the pool. Lo! He was no longer a gray bird, awkward and ugly. He himself was a swan!

Good fortune was his at last, and instantly all his troubles were forgotten. The other swans stroked his glossy feathers lovingly with their bills. Then some children came running. "See the new swan!" they cried. "He is much handsomer than the others."

The young swan held his graceful head high. His heart beat with rapture as he exclaimed, "I never dreamed of so much happiness when I was an ugly duckling!"

The Golden Eggs

Many, many years ago a farmer and his good wife dwelt in a humble cottage beside a winding stream. The couple lacked many things that their richer neighbors enjoyed. But they were always willing to share what they had.

No matter how little they had themselves, they always spared a bit of food for the wild creatures that drank from the stream. The good wife never neglected to toss a handful of crumbs to the robins and wrens. She also scattered grain on the riverbank for the wild fowls.

One day a splendid wild goose flew down to the farmyard. She did not fly off again but made herself quite at home. Soon she had settled down in a dust-wallow with the hens.

The next morning when the wife heard the hens cackling, she went out to get the eggs. She saw the big wild goose fly off a nest, looking extremely wise.

"Oho!" exclaimed the woman. "A goose egg! It will fetch a good price."

She hurried to the nest. There in the hay lay an egg of solid gold! The woman was so excited that she screamed for her husband, who was weeding a cabbage patch.

"G-G-G-Goose! S-S-S-Solid gold egg!" she stuttered, almost speechless.

"Have the fairies bewitched your tongue?" he asked. "What are you stuttering about?"

Speaking more calmly, she said, "The wild goose has just laid an egg of solid gold."

"Solid gold!" cried the man. "Where?"

"I-I-In the barn," she stuttered.

"Simpleton!" shrieked her husband. "Do you lack good sense? Why did you leave a solid gold egg in the barn, where a common thief might steal it?"

He rushed into the barn and picked up the golden egg. How it glittered! The farmer was nearly overcome with rapture.

"We must conceal this rare treasure," he cried. "Some dishonest person will try to steal it."

They chose a hiding place under the clay bricks of the hearth. Marveling at their good fortune, they thought about the egg all day. They neglected their work and forgot to feed their chickens and the wild creatures. When night came, they could not sleep for wondering if they would find another gold egg the following day.

The next morning they rose before dawn. Carrying a lantern, they ran to the barn. There lay a second glittering egg of solid gold. The couple's rapture knew no bounds as they regarded the treasure.

Day after day the wild goose laid an egg of purest gold. Day after day the greedy partners buried the egg and lingered in the house to guard the treasure. They neglected their work. They forgot that the chickens and wild fowls lacked food. They were bewitched by dazzling dreams of rare wealth.

"I shall soon be the wealthiest man in all the land," boasted the farmer. Hooking his thumbs over his belt, he tried to reckon the worth of his treasure. He could buy choice food, fine horses, a carriage, and anything else he chose. But suddenly he felt that he could not endure waiting another instant for this great wealth.

"I'll cut the goose open and get all her eggs at once," he cried. So he rushed out and killed the goose. Cutting her open, he discovered she was like any common goose!

"Alas and alack!" he cried in despair. "Why did I kill the goose that laid the golden eggs? If I had not been so greedy, I could have improved my good fortune. At least I've learned a lesson. Things worth having are worth waiting for."

Cinder Lad

The Mystery of the Hayfield

Once there was a man who had a meadow that he prized highly for its fine hay. But one Midsummer's Eve, when the grass was at its best, the meadow was eaten down to the ground. It looked like a pasture where a whole flock of sheep had been grazing.

The same thing occurred a second year. The poor man felt that he could not endure having his crop ruined a third time. So the next year on Midsummer's Eve, he told his sons that one of them must hide in the barn to watch the hayfield.

The eldest son went off to the barn. As he watched the hay, suddenly there came the sound of booming thunder. Then the very planks of the floor rattled and creaked as if from the shock of an earthquake. The lad took to his heels in fright. Nor did he dare to look around until he got home. So the hay disappeared again.

The fourth year on Midsummer's Eve, the next eldest son went to guard the meadow.

Again came the booming thunder. The lad took to his heels as if bewitched, and the hay was destroyed as before.

On Midsummer's Eve of the fifth year, the turn came to Cinder Lad, the youngest son. But when he prepared to go, his brothers sneered at him. "What a fine guard you'll make!" they cried. "All you've ever done is sit on a stool among the cinders."

In spite of their teasing, Cinder Lad did not despair but went to the barn. Soon the booming and creaking and quaking began.

"Well," said Cinder Lad, "if nothing worse than this happens, I can stand it."

But the uproar grew worse. Suddenly the booming and the quaking ceased. The air was deathly still. Instead of fleeing, Cinder Lad tiptoed to the half-open barn door and peeked out.

There stood a spanking big horse. It was eating away as if it would never stop. One glance convinced Cinder Lad that this was no ordinary horse. It wore bright-colored harness, and beside it lay a sword and a suit of glittering brass armor for a knight.

"Ah!" said the lad. "So it's you who eats our grass. Well, I'll attend to you." And he proceeded to conceal both horse and armor in a secret place.

When Cinder Lad got home, his father and brothers questioned him closely. But he did not relate his true adventures. He merely claimed that he had heard nothing frightening. The brothers suspected that he was not telling the truth. However, there was the meadow grass, still thick and green.

The next year on Midsummer's Eve, the two elder brothers again lacked courage to watch the meadow. So Cinder Lad went to the barn. A storm came up as before. But compared to these violent creaks and blasts, last year's uproar had been a mere whisper.

All at once the air was still. Cinder Lad looked out. There stood another giant steed. He, too, was eating away at a great rate. He was far handsomer than the horse that had appeared the year before, and of a size rarely seen. Beside him lay a suit of silver armor for a knight.

"Ah!" said the lad. "So now it's you who eats our grass. I'll attend to you." He led this horse to the place where he had hidden the other. Then he returned home.

Again his elder brothers sneered at him. "Well," said one of them, "I suppose you'll claim there's no damage to our hayfield."

"That I do!" declared Cinder Lad. And he showed no further concern in the matter.

But the others, suspecting his word, went to the meadow. Lo and behold! There stood the grass, thicker and greener than ever.

The next year the two elder brothers were still afraid. So Cinder Lad was required to watch the field. Again came the peals of thunder, the creaking and quaking, and the silence. When the brave lad looked out, he saw a horse far finer and glossier than the others. Near him lay armor of purest gold.

Cinder Lad proceeded to hide the horse and went to report that the hay was safe.

The Trials at the Glass Hill

The king of the country where Cinder Lad dwelt had a daughter who was beautiful beyond compare. The king proclaimed that the princess should marry the first man in the realm who could ride up a glass hill as slippery as ice.

The king further proclaimed that the princess would sit at the top of the hill holding three golden apples in her lap. Whoever could ride up the slippery hill and carry off the golden apples was to claim the princess for his bride and half the kingdom besides.

Everyone—young or old, rich or poor—was invited to attend the trials.

Knights and princes from the whole realm accepted the king's invitation, and everyone came to watch the rare sight. The two elder brothers, neglecting their work, were among the watchers. But they had refused sneeringly to let Cinder Lad accompany them.

All day long the gallant noblemen sought to climb the glass hill. No one, however, could proceed even twice the length of his horse. So the king announced that no further trials would be held until the next day.

Suddenly a knight in glittering brass armor appeared. Up the slippery hill he charged at full speed. Sparks flew from the hoofs of his splendid horse as he proceeded about a third of the way.

When the princess beheld the knight in the brass armor, she wished that he might claim her for his wife. But the horse came a third of the way and no farther. Then back he slipped. Quickly the princess flung one of her golden apples after the strange knight. It fell right into his lap.

When the knight reached the foot of the hill, he galloped off before anyone could prevent his disappearance.

The next day the two brothers, neglecting their work as before, set off to attend the trials. Cinder Lad pleaded to go with them. They would have none of him.

Once again the knights and princes tried to urge their steeds up the hill. They rode and slipped and slipped and rode. But not one could force his panting horse up the steep slope.

All at once a knight in silver armor came riding into the midst of the watching throng. His horse was black and of uncommon size. Straight toward the slippery hill the knight charged, riding directly up two-thirds of the way.

Suddenly the black horse wheeled with his forefeet in the air.

The princess gazed with rapture at the gallant rider. Before he had turned around, she had sprung to her feet and thrown the second apple to him. But as soon as the knight reached the foot of the hill, he rode swiftly away.

On the third day everything occurred as on the two days before. Cinder Lad again begged to go with his brothers. Again they would not permit him to accompany them.

The gallant knights renewed their efforts to climb the hill. No one could improve on his attempt of the day before. No one got farther than a quarter of the way up.

At last a knight came riding on a horse so huge that no one had ever seen its equal. This mysterious knight wore armor of pure gold. It was so bright that the sun's rays gleamed from it a mile off.

Up the slippery hill he went at full speed. He took the third apple from the princess in triumph. Then he rode down and was gone before anyone could halt him.

Now when the elder brothers got home that evening, they told and retold the tale of the knight in golden armor. Cinder Lad listened as if bewitched.

"I vow no one has ever possessed such glorious armor before!" one brother cried. "Not even in the whole world!"

"I-I wish I could have seen him," Cinder Lad stuttered.

"You!" sneered the eldest brother. "Why, the knight wouldn't even have glanced at a stuttering simpleton like you."

The next day the king's messenger sought out all the knights, ordering them to come to the palace. Among them the king hoped to find the one who had climbed the hill.

So to the palace they all came. But not a single one possessed a golden apple. Nor could any of them explain the disappearance of the mysterious knight.

"Alas! Alack!" cried the king in despair. "Where is the gallant knight in the golden armor?"

Then the king commanded that everybody in all the realm should be sought out and brought to the palace. There were knights and ladies, cooks, carpenters, innkeepers, bootblacks, maid-servants, and many others. But none had seen the golden apples. No one knew who the golden knight might be, for his armor had covered him from head to toe. Therefore no one had caught even a glimpse of his face.

The two brothers of Cinder Lad were the last ones to be questioned. But of course they knew nothing of the golden apples nor of the knight.

"Is there no one else in all my kingdom?" asked the despairing king. "I am requiring every one of my people to come before me."

"Oh," said the eldest brother, "there's our young brother. But he could not have seen the golden apples. I'm sure he has not left his chimney corner for the last three days."

"Never mind that," said the king. "Fetch him to me without further delay."

The two brothers ran home to fetch Cinder Lad. They dragged him to the king, dressed just as he was in a ragged old cloak.

"Speak out, lad," ordered the king when Cinder Lad came to the foot of the throne. "Have you seen the golden apples?"

"Yes, Your Majesty," replied Cinder Lad. "I have the apples. Here is the first one. Here is the second. And here is the third."

The youth took off his ragged cloak. Now he stood before the king dressed in glorious armor of pure gold.

"Ah!" exclaimed the king in great delight. "You shall marry my daughter and rule the southern half of my realm. So gallant a knight well deserves a rich reward."

BOOKS TO READ

Here are some good books that provide more of the same fun and adventure we find in *More Times and Places*.

Young Citizens Here and There

Across Canada. Clare Bice.
This book contains eight interesting stories, all by the same author, about boys and girls who live in different parts of Canada. The story called "The Quiet Mountains" in *More Times and Places* is taken from this book.

Blue Willow. Doris Gates.
Janey belongs to a family of crop harvesters who have always moved about from place to place, following the crops. Janey longs for a real home worthy of her precious blue willow plate. She finally wins such a home for her family, and finds true friends among her California neighbors.

Cowboy Boots. Shannon Garst.
Here is a story about a city boy's visit to a ranch and his struggles to earn the right to be called a cowboy.

Here's a Penny. Carolyn Haywood.
This is the first of three very funny books about Penny and Peter, whom you have already met in *More Times and Places*. The two boys become brothers by being adopted into the same family. *Penny and Peter*, from which the story "Unwelcome Passengers" was taken, and *Penny Goes to Camp* contain more of the brothers' amusing adventures.

Maggie Rose, Her Birthday Christmas. Ruth Sawyer.
Maggie Rose is a little New England girl who is determined to have a very special Christmas birthday party. Her lazy, loving family think she is clever but do nothing to help her with her exciting plans until her hard-earned money is stolen. How she has her wonderful party at last makes a funny, sad, and beautiful Christmas story.

Mountain Born. Elizabeth Yates.
This is the first of two books about Peter, whose father has a mountain farm in New England. In this book Peter learns to care for the sheep and has some very exciting adventures. In the second book, *A Place for Peter*, the boy proves that he can be trusted with important farm tasks and is finally recognized as his father's partner.

Peachtree Island. Mildred Lawrence.
Cissie, who has no parents, spends a year on her uncle's peach orchard in the Great Lakes region. She thinks her uncle prefers boys to girls, and does all she can to make him change his mind. Her success brings Cissie a very happy surprise.

Prairie School. Lois Lenski.
Here is the true and exciting story of a group of school children and their teacher. It tells of their troubles and courage during a hard, snowy winter on the prairies of South Dakota.

The School Train. Helen Acker.
Two brothers, the sons of a fur-trapper, walk twenty miles through the deep forests of Canada to catch up with the school train. The story by the same name in *More Times and Places* is a shortened form of this unusual book.

Told under Spacious Skies. Association for Childhood Education. This collection of twenty-seven stories, by well-known authors, is about children living in different regions of the United States. Each story tells about something that has to do with a special region.

When the Moon Is New. Laura Bannon.
An Indian girl in Florida is promised a big surprise "when the moon is new." She hopes that the surprise will be a sewing machine, but it turns out to be something much better. You will enjoy the pictures of the Florida Everglades and of the colorful Indian costumes.

The Great Outdoors

An Otter's Story.   Emil E. Liers.

The author of this book has pet otters. In writing about the life of two young river otters, he shows us how harmless and playful these animals are. The things that happen in the story are based on actual facts.

Brighty of the Grand Canyon.   Marguerite Henry.

A little wild burro called Brighty is the hero of this story. All by himself, he makes a now-famous trail from the top to the bottom of the Grand Canyon. Brighty has many adventures, among them a fight with a mountain lion. You will enjoy the funny pictures showing how Uncle Jim takes care of Brighty's wounds. Part of the story is a mystery, and Uncle Jim is the one who solves it.

Dash and Dart.   Mary and Conrad Buff.

This beautiful picture-story of the first year in the life of twin fawns tells how the young fawns learn the things they should know. Occasionally the authors feel that the fawns think as people do. For example, Dash admires his father's big, handsome antlers but does not realize what is happening when his own antlers begin to grow.

Honk, the Moose.   Phil Stong.

Honk will be one of your favorite animals after you have read this very funny story. It is about a wild moose that moves into a village stable for the winter and makes himself at home. Not even the village policemen can manage to get him out.

Let Them Live.   Dorothy Lathrop.

You will understand why the author is famous for her beautiful pictures when you see this book. *Let Them Live* explains why such wild animals as red foxes, beavers, wood ducks, sea otters, black bears, fur seals, and mountain lions should not be hunted and killed as they are today.

Snow Dog.   Jim Kjelgaard.

The Husky puppy of "Wilderness Partners" in *More Times and Places* is the "snow dog" of this story. The book will tell you how he later meets a northern trapper who tries hard to make friends with the dog. You will like the exciting ending.

Spike, the Story of a Whitetail Deer.   Robert McClung.

All the facts in Mr. McClung's stories are correct, and this deer story is one of his best. It tells how a deer changes in appearance as he grows older, and how he learns to take care of himself. It also describes the dangers he faces from forest fires and from hunters who do not obey the game laws.

Star of Wild Horse Canyon.   Clyde Bulla.

Here a boy has a chance to see a herd of wild horses captured, and later to train one of them himself. One stormy night the horse, Star, disappears. What do you suppose happens when Danny discovers that someone is hiding Star from him?

The Biggest Bear on Earth.   Harold McCracken.

An Alaskan brown bear cub whose mother is killed grows up to be the biggest bear in the world and certainly one of the smartest and strongest. After a fight with another huge bear, he rules as king of the forest.

The Blind Colt.   Glen Rounds.

You cannot help liking this fine story of how a colt learns to get along without sight and of a young boy's understanding love for him. You will also want to read *The Stolen Pony*, by the same author.

The Wild Little Honker.   Dorothy Childs Hogner.

A family of wild geese settles down contentedly on a river in New York State. Only Little Honker scorns their easy life. Finally he flies off with some geese that are returning to their home in the far North.

Famous Americans of Other Times

Abraham Lincoln: An Initial Biography.   Genevieve Foster.
This book and *George Washington: An Initial Biography*, by
the same author, will tell you about the lives of two of our
country's best-loved men. Both of these fine books have
pictures by the author.

Benjamin Franklin.   Ingri and Edgar d'Aulaire.
It is hard to tell the whole story of Franklin's life in a short
book with large pictures, but this one tells a surprising
amount. Be sure to notice Franklin's sayings tucked away
around the borders of the pages.

Betsy Ross and the Flag.   Jane Mayer.
How we first got our flag is not known exactly, but here is a
well-known story told in an interesting way.

Boat Builder, the Story of Robert Fulton.   Clara Ingram Judson.
Robert Fulton's life was indeed a busy one. Here Mrs.
Judson describes his youth and his work both as an artist
and as an inventor. "Fulton's Folly" in *More Times and
Places* is taken from *Boat Builder*.

Buffalo Bill.   Ingri and Edgar d'Aulaire.
Buffalo Bill was a mighty man of the plains and a showman
as well. In this book you will follow his exciting life from
childhood to his days with circuses and rodeos. The pictures
are large and colorful.

Clara Barton: Girl Nurse.   Augusta Stevenson.
This is a story about Clara Barton's childhood. The author
has also written about the childhoods of other famous Americans. You will like *Abe Lincoln: Frontier Boy* and *George
Washington: Boy Leader*.

George Washington, Leader of the People.   Clara Ingram Judson.
In this book, from which the story "George Grows Up" in
More Times and Places is taken, the author makes George
Washington seem as real as if he were still alive. You will

enjoy equally well Mrs. Judson's *Abraham Lincoln, Friend of the People.*

Kit Carson, Mountain Man.   Margaret E. Bell.
The old days of the West are brought to life in this book about one of our country's greatest scouts and hunters. Again and again young Kit Carson was refused a chance to prove his scouting skill to the fur-trapping mountain men, but success came at last.

Martin and Abraham Lincoln.   Catherine Coblentz.
This is the true story of a boy who was given comfort in time of trouble by a kindly man who turned out to be the President of the United States.

The Story of Daniel Boone.   William O. Steele.
Here you will read about Daniel's boyhood, his adventures with the Indians, and the settling of Kentucky.

The Story of John Paul Jones.   Iris Vinton.
This book will tell you how a lively boy named John Paul Jones grew up to be one of America's most famous heroes of the sea.

The Story of Mad Anthony Wayne.   Hazel Wilson.
Anthony Wayne was one of George Washington's greatest and most daring generals. In this story of his life you will learn of his great concern for the well-being of his men, and of their willingness to follow him on his maddest adventures.

The Story of Thomas Alva Edison.   Enid La Monte Meadowcroft.   The author tells in an entertaining way about Edison's experiments, from a boyhood attempt to turn a friend into a balloon to his invention of moving pictures. The Edison story in *More Times and Places* is from this book.

Tom Edison: Boy Inventor.   Sue Guthridge.
Here is another good book about Thomas Edison. This one is entirely about his childhood.

Old Tales from Everywhere

Aesop's Fables. Thomas James and George Tyler Townsend. There are many other beautiful books containing Aesop's fables, but you will especially like the pictures in this book and the way the fables are told.

Chimney Corner Fairy Tales. Veronica Hutchinson. Here is a good collection of a few favorite stories with pleasant pictures.

East of the Sun and West of the Moon. Peter Asbjörnsen and Jörgen Moe. Retold by Edgar and Ingri d'Aulaire. When stories are written in a different language from ours, like the tales in this book, someone has to retell them for us in English. Many of these stories are retold by Gudrun Thorne-Thomsen in a book with almost the same name: *East o' the Sun and West o' the Moon.*

English Fairy Tales. Joseph Jacobs. Forty-three old English fairy tales appear in this book, and another forty-four in *More English Fairy Tales.* A small book called *Dick Whittington and His Cat* contains only this one famous old English tale, retold by Marcia Brown. Be sure to read it.

Fairy Tales. Hans Christian Andersen. Retold by Mrs. E. V. Lucas and Mrs. H. B. Paull. Andersen was a famous writer of fairy tales, and there are many thick books full of his stories. There are also small books, with just one story beautifully pictured, that you may prefer. Try these: *The Emperor's New Clothes* (pictures by Virginia Lee Burton); *The Steadfast Tin Soldier* (pictures by Marcia Brown); *The Ugly Duckling* (pictures by Will Nickless).

Grimms' Fairy Tales. Jacob and Wilhelm Grimm. Retold by Mrs. E. V. Lucas, Lucy Crane, and Marian Edwardes. Among the most exciting fairy tales are those collected by the Grimm brothers. Here are many of their stories, with amusing pictures. Other good collections with fewer stories are *Tales from Grimm, More Tales from Grimm,* and *Three Gay Tales from Grimm,* by Wanda Gág. *Gone Is Gone,* also by Wanda Gág, is just one tale.

Padre Porko, the Gentlemanly Pig. Robert Davis.
In all these old tales from Spain, the "gentlemanly pig" is called upon to get the other animals out of trouble. The stories are great fun.

Peter and the Wolf. Serge Prokofieff.
Some of you will be familiar with this fairy tale from hearing it on the radio or on a record. Here it is in a small book, with many delightful pictures by Warren Chappell. The book also contains some of the most important parts of the music.

Picture Tales from Spain. Retold by Ruth Sawyer.
These eleven easy-to-read tales are fun to tell and still more fun to act out.

Puss in Boots. Charles Perrault.
The pictures by Marcia Brown make this one of the gayest and handsomest books you have ever seen. It is easy to read, too.

Tales of Faraway Folk. Babette Deutsch and Avrahm Yarmolinsky. You are sure to be entertained by these tales from many lands.

The Three Sneezes and Other Swiss Tales. Roger Duvoisin.
Here are some exciting old Swiss tales, simply told.

Time to Laugh. Phyllis Fenner.
When you read these stories collected from many parts of the world, you will agree with the author that laughter is the same everywhere. Two of Phyllis Fenner's other collections are *Giants, Witches, and a Dragon or Two* and *Princesses and Peasant Boys.*

GLOSSARY

Full Pronunciation Key

The pronunciation of each word is shown just after the word, in this way: **ab bre vi ate** (ə brē′vi āt). The letters and signs used are pronounced as in the words below. The mark ′ is placed after a syllable with primary or heavy accent, as in the example above. The mark ′ after a syllable shows a secondary or lighter accent, as in **ab bre vi a tion** (ə brē′vi ā′shən).

a	hat, cap	j	jam, enjoy	u	cup, butter
ā	age, face	k	kind, seek	u̇	full, put
ã	care, air	l	land, coal	ü	rule, move
ä	father, far	m	me, am	ū	use, music
		n	no, in		
b	bad, rob	ng	long, bring		
ch	child, much			v	very, save
d	did, red	o	hot, rock	w	will, woman
		ō	open, go	y	young, yet
e	let, best	ô	order, all		
ē	equal, be	oi	oil, voice	z	zero, breeze
ėr	term, learn	ou	house, out	zh	measure, seizure
f	fat, if	p	paper, cup	ə	represents:
g	go, bag	r	run, try		a in about
h	he, how	s	say, yes		e in taken
		sh	she, rush		i in pencil
i	it, pin	t	tell, it		o in lemon
ī	ice, five	th	thin, both		u in circus
		ᵺ	then, smooth		

This pronunciation key is from the *Thorndike-Barnhart Beginning Dictionary*. Special acknowledgment is made to Clarence L. Barnhart, editor of the Thorndike-Barnhart Dictionaries, for his assistance in the preparation of this glossary.

a broad (ə brôd′), outside one's country. He is going abroad this summer to travel in England.

ac com pa ny (ə kum′pə ni), go along with. He will accompany you on your walk. The rain was accompanied by a high wind.

a corn (ā′kôrn), the nut of an oak tree.

Acorn

ad vance (ad vans′), 1. move forward.. 2. forward movement. The army's advance was very slow. 3. **In advance** means in front, or ahead of time.

a lert (ə lèrt′), 1. watchful; wide-awake. 2. lively. 3. **On the alert** means watchful.

al li ga tor (al′ə gā′tər), large crawling animal with a long body, four short legs, a thick skin, and a long tail. See the picture. Alligators live in rivers and swamps of warm parts of America.

Alligator (12 ft. long)

am ble (am′bəl), go in a slow, easy way.

ap par ent ly (ə par′ənt li), 1. as far as one can tell; seemingly. 2. clearly; plainly.

ar mor (är′mər), covering worn to protect the body in fighting.

ar riv al (ə rĭv′əl), coming. She is waiting for the arrival of the steamboat.

as sist (ə sist′), help.

at tack (ə tak′), 1. set upon to hurt; go against as an enemy. The dog attacked the cat.

---

2. begin to work on; as, to attack a hard lesson. 3. attacking. The attack of the enemy took us by surprise.

au di ence (ô′di əns), all the people gathered in a place or building to hear or see (someone or something).

ban ner (ban′ər), flag. Robert carried our school banner in the parade.

be held (bi held′), saw. They beheld the approaching storm.

be hold (bi hōld′), see; look; take notice. Behold! the king!

belt (belt), 1. strip of leather, cloth, etc., worn around the body to hold in or support clothes. 2. region in which certain crops or plants grow well. The wheat belt is the region where wheat is grown.

be ware (bi wãr′), be careful; be on your guard against. Beware! danger is here. Beware the dog!

be witch (bi wich′), 1. put under a spell; use magic on. The wicked fairy bewitched the princess, and made her fall into a long sleep. 2. delight very much. We were all bewitched by our pretty little cousin.

blast (blast), 1. strong sudden rush of wind or air; as, the icy blasts of winter. 2. sound made by blowing a horn or trumpet. We heard the blast of the trumpet.

bolt (bōlt), dash off; run away.

bore[1] (bôr), make a hole in anything with a tool that turns; hollow out evenly like a tube.

bore² (bôr), make weary by tiresome talk or by being dull. This book bores me; so I shall not finish it.

bound a ry (boun′də ri), anything that shows the border of a piece of land or a region. A river sometimes forms the boundary between two states.

brief (brēf), short.

bril liant (bril′yənt), 1. sparkling; very bright. 2. splendid.

cac tus (kak′təs), thorny plant without leaves. Cactuses grow in dry, hot regions.

Common cactus

can yon (kan′yən), narrow valley with high, steep sides, usually with a stream at the bottom.

cease (sēs), stop.

coil (koil), 1. wind round and round into a circle, a pile, or a curl. A snake can coil itself up or coil around a branch. A wire spring is evenly coiled. 2. anything that is coiled; as, a coil of rope.

com mu ni ty (kə mū′nə ti), the people of any small region or town. This lake provides water for six communities.

com pan ion (kəm pan′yən), one who goes along with or accompanies another; one who shares in what another is doing. The twins were companions in work and play.

com ple tion (kəm plē′shən), 1. finishing; act of completing. After the completion of the job,

the workman went home. 2. being finished or completed. The work is near completion.

con ceal (kən sēl′), hide.

con cern (kən sėrn′), 1. worry. 2. interest.

con fuse (kən fūz′), 1. mix up; throw into disorder. So many people talking to me at once confused me. 2. mistake (one thing for another). People often confuse Mary with her sister.

con sid er (kən sid′ər), 1. think about in order to decide. Take till tonight to consider my offer. 2. think to be. I consider him an able man. 3. allow for; take into account. This watch runs well, if you consider how old it is.

con vince (kən vins′), make someone feel sure; persuade firmly.

coon (kün), raccoon, a small grayish animal with a bushy ringed tail.

cove (kōv), small bay; mouth of a creek; inlet on the shore.

coy o te (kī ō′ti or kī′ōt), prairie wolf of western North America.

crab (krab), water animal with eight legs, two claws, and a broad, flat, shell covering. Many kinds of crabs are good to eat.

Crab

craft y (kraf′ti), clever at fooling others; sly; as, the crafty fox.

creak (krēk), 1. squeak loudly. 2. creaking noise.

crick et (krik′it), black insect of the grasshopper family.

crouch (krouch), 1. stoop low with bent legs like an animal ready to spring, or like a person hiding. 2. shrink down in fear.

cy press (sī′prəs), evergreen tree with hard wood and dark leaves.

deck (dek), floor of a ship.

de part (di pärt′), go away; leave. We arrived in the village in the morning, and departed at night.

de spair (di spâr′), 1. loss of hope; a being without hope; a dreadful feeling that nothing good can happen. Despair seized us as we felt the boat sinking under us. 2. lose hope. The doctors despaired of saving the child's life.

des per ate (des′pər it), 1. frantic. 2. hopeless. 3. ready to run any risk; as, a desperate thief.

de ter mine (di tėr′mən), make up one's mind very firmly. He determined to become the best Scout in his troop.

dis mal (diz′məl), 1. dark; gloomy. A rainy day is dismal. 2. dreary; miserable. Sickness or bad luck often makes a person feel dismal.

dis play (dis plā′), 1. show. He displayed his good nature by answering all our questions. 2. planned showing of a thing, for some special purpose. Grade 5 had two displays of children's drawings.

dis tress (dis tres′), 1. great pain or sorrow; worry; trouble. 2. make unhappy; worry.

dou ble (dub′əl), 1. twice as great, as large, as strong, etc. 2. made of two like parts; in a pair; as, double doors. 3. bend or turn sharply backward. The fox doubled on his track and escaped the dogs.

Dr., Doctor.

drake (drāk), male duck.

drawl (drôl), 1. talk in a slow, lazy way. 2. slow, lazy way of talking.

dread (dred), 1. look forward to with fear or dislike; fear greatly. Cats dread water. 2. fear, especially fear of something that will happen, or may happen.

dread ful (dred′fəl), terrible; fearful.

drear y (drēr′i), gloomy and dull; without cheer.

dusk (dusk), 1. the time just before dark. 2. shade; gloom.

dwarf (dwôrf), 1. person, animal, or plant much below the usual size for its kind. 2. in fairy tales, an ugly little man with magic power.

dwelt (dwelt), lived; made one's home. We have dwelt in the country for years.

ear nest (ėr′nist), 1. serious; strong and firm in purpose. An earnest pupil has his mind on his work. 2. **In earnest** means determined.

hat, āge, cãre, fär; let, bē, tėrm; it, īce; hot, ōpen, ôrder; oil, out; cup, pút, rüle, ūse; takən

earth quake (ėrth′kwāk′), shaking or sliding of the ground, caused by changes far beneath the surface. Earthquakes sometimes destroy whole cities.

ech o (ek′ō), repeat; be heard again.

eld er (el′dər), older.

eld est (el′dist), oldest.

en dure (en dür′ or en dūr′), 1. last; keep on. A gold ring will endure for a thousand years. 2. bear; stand. The Indians could endure much pain.

en rage (en rāj′), make very angry; make furious.

ex hib it (eg zib′it), 1. show to the public. You should exhibit your roses in the Flower Show. 2. something shown to the public. Their exhibit of corn at the fair won the prize.

ex per i ment (eks per′ə ment for 1, eks per′ə mənt for 2), 1. try in order to find out; make tests. That man is experimenting with dyes to get the color that he wants. 2. trial or test to find out something; as, a cooking experiment.

ex treme ly (eks trēm′li), much more than usual; very.

faith ful (fāth′fəl), loyal; as, a faithful friend, a faithful servant.

fal ter (fôl′tər), 1. hesitate; lose courage. The soldiers faltered for a moment as their captain fell. 2. become unsteady in movement.

fa mil iar (fə mil′yər), 1. well known. The words of the old song were familiar to everyone.

2. well acquainted. He was familiar with several languages.

fee ble (fē′bəl), weak; as, a feeble old man, a feeble cry.

fetch (fech), go and get; bring. Please fetch me my glasses.

flap jack (flap′jak′), pancake.

fled (fled), 1. ran away. The thieves fled, but they were soon caught. 2. went quickly.

flee (flē), 1. run away. 2. go quickly.

fleet[1] (flēt), ships under one command; ships sailing together; as, the American fleet.

fleet[2] (flēt), fast moving; rapid.

fod der (fod′ər), coarse food for horses, cattle, etc. Hay and cornstalks with their leaves are fodder.

fol ly (fol′i), 1. being foolish; lack of sense. It is folly to eat too much. 2. foolish practice, act, or idea; something silly. "You are too old for such follies," said Mother.

for tune (fôr′chən), 1. great deal of money; riches. 2. luck; chance.

fos sil (fos′əl), the hardened remains of an animal or plant. Fossils of ferns are found in coal.

frame (frām), 1. support over which something is stretched or built; as, the frame of a house. 2. put a border around; as, to frame a picture.

freak (frēk), something very queer or unusual. A green leaf growing in the middle of a rose would be called a freak of nature.

fre quent (frē′kwənt for 1, fri kwent′ for 2), 1. happening

306

often, near together, or every little while. Storms are frequent in March. 2. be often in; go to often. Frogs frequent ponds.

fre quent ly (frē′kwənt li), often.

fu ture (fū′chər), 1. the time to come. 2. coming. We hope your future years will all be happy.

gal lant (gal′ənt), brave.

gan der (gan′dər), male goose.

glimpse (glimps), 1. very brief view; short look. I got a glimpse of the falls as our train went by. 2. catch a brief view of. I glimpsed her dress as she went by.

glit ter (glit′ər), 1. shine with a bright, sparkling light. 2. bright, sparkling light.

glo ri ous (glô′ri əs), magnificent; splendid.

gloss y (glôs′i), smooth and shiny.

gov ern ment (guv′ərn mənt), person or persons ruling or managing a country at any time.

grad u al ly (graj′ü əl i), little by little.

griz zly (griz′li), large, fierce bear of western North America. See the picture.

gul ly (gul′i), little steep valley; ditch.

Grizzly bear (about 8 ft. long)

harsh (härsh), 1. rough to the touch, taste, eye, or ear; as, a harsh voice, a harsh wind. 2. cruel.

heed (hēd), 1. take notice of. Now heed what I say. 2. careful attention. She pays heed to her clothes.

hes i tate (hez′ə tāt), 1. hold back; be undecided; feel doubtful. 2. stop an instant; pause.

hith er (hiŦH′ər), 1. here. 2. **Hither and thither** means here and there.

hum ble (hum′bəl), 1. simple; not important; not grand. We live in a humble cottage of one room. 2. not proud.

hum bly (hum′bli), in a humble manner.

Husk y or **husk y** (hus′ki), Eskimo dog.

im prove (im prüv′), 1. make better. You could improve your handwriting if you tried. 2. become better; as, to improve in health.

in tent (in tent′), 1. paying close attention; earnest. 2. much interested. She is intent on doing her best.

jeer (jēr), make fun in a rude or unkind way. Do not jeer at the mistakes or misfortunes of others.

keen (kēn), 1. so shaped as to cut well; as, a keen knife. 2. sharp; cutting; as, keen wit, keen pain. 3. able to do its work quickly and exactly; as, a keen mind, keen eyes.

---

hat, āge, cãre, fär; let, bē, tèrm; it, īce; hot, ōpen, ôrder; oil, out; cup, pút, rüle, ūse; takən

307

lack (lak), have no; be without. The desert lacks water.

lamp (lamp), a gas, oil, or electric light. See the picture.

Oil lamp

lass (las), girl; young girl.

ledge (lej), 1. narrow shelf; as, a window ledge. 2. shelf of rock.

lin ger (ling′gər), stay on; go slowly, as if unwilling to leave.

lo (lō), look! see!

loon (lün), large diving bird that has a loud, wild cry. See the picture.

Loon (about 32 in. long)

lord (lôrd), 1. owner, ruler, or master; person who has the power. 2. title of some noblemen.

lunge (lunj), 1. sudden forward movement. 2. move forward suddenly.

lurk (lèrk), stay about without attracting attention; be hidden. A tiger was lurking in the forest outside the village.

mad am (mad′əm), polite title used in speaking of a lady or to a lady.

mare (mãr), female horse.

mar vel (mär′vəl), 1. wonderful thing. The airplane, radio, and television are among the marvels of science. 2. wonder greatly.

ma te ri al (mə tēr′i əl), what a thing is made from or done with; as, dress material, building materials, writing materials.

meek (mēk), 1. gentle; patient; not easily angered. 2. giving in tamely when ordered about.

mes quite (mes kēt′), tree or shrub common in the southwestern United States. Cattle eat mesquite pods.

midg et (mij′it), very small person; dwarf.

midst (midst), middle. **In our midst** means among us.

mid sum mer (mid′ sum′ər), 1. the middle of summer. 2. in the middle of summer. 3. the time near June 21.

mu se um (mū zē′əm), building or rooms in which collections and objects of interest are kept and exhibited.

neg lect (ni glekt′), 1. give too little care or attention to. 2. leave undone. 3. fail. Don't neglect to water the plants.

no ble man (nō′bəl mən), man of noble title or birth.

ob serve (əb zèrv′), 1. notice. Did you observe anything strange about that man? 2. examine closely; study.

oc ca sion al ly (ə kā′zhən əl i), now and then; once in a while.

oc cur (ə kèr′), 1. happen; take place. Is anything important occurring on Friday? 2. come to mind; suggest itself. A new idea suddenly occurred to me.

oc to pus (ok′tə pəs), sea animal having a soft body and eight arms with suckers on them.

o dor (ō′dər), smell; as, the odor of roses.

op por tu ni ty (op′ər tü′nə ti or op′ər tü′nə ti), good chance. I had an opportunity to earn some money picking berries.

op po site (op′ə zit), across from; facing. The teacher's desk was opposite the door.

or chard (ôr′chərd), piece of ground on which fruit trees are grown.

o ver come (ō′vər kum′), 1. get the better of. We can overcome difficulties. Overcome by the sight of so much candy, the child grabbed for it. 2. made weak or helpless. The child was overcome by weariness and slept.

pan ic (pan′ik), sudden, terrible fear.

pa trol (pə trōl′), 1. go the rounds as a watchman or a policeman does. The camp was carefully patrolled. 2. men who patrol. The patrol was changed at midnight.

pause (pôz), stop for a time; wait. He made a short pause and then went on reading. The dog paused when he heard me.

peer (pēr), 1. look closely to see clearly, as a near-sighted person does. She peered at the tag to read the price. 2. peep out. The sun was peering from behind a cloud.

per mis sion (pər mish′ən), consent; leave; permitting. He asked the teacher's permission to go early.

per mit (pər mit′ for 1, pėr′mit for 2), 1. let; allow. Mr. Bell permitted us to swim in his pond. 2. written order giving permission to do something. Have you a permit to fish in the lake?

pierce (pērs), 1. make a hole in; bore into or through. A nail pierced the tire of our car. 2. make a way through with the eye or mind; as, to pierce a disguise, to pierce a mystery.

pit y (pit′i), 1. sorrow for another's distress or suffering; a feeling for the sorrows of others. 2. feel sorry for. Ann pitied any child who was hurt or hungry. 3. cause for pity or distress. It is a pity to be kept in the house in fine weather.

plead (plēd), ask earnestly; beg. The busy man pleaded for more time to finish the job.

plume (plüm), 1. feather; a large, long feather. 2. something like a large soft feather; as, a plume of smoke.

por trait (pôr′trit or pôr′trāt), picture of a person.

pos sess (pə zes′), own; have. The farmer possessed many acres of land.

pounce (pouns), jump suddenly and seize. The cat pounced upon the mouse.

prey (prā), 1. animal hunted or seized for food. Mice and birds are the prey of cats. 2. hunt and seize for food. Cats prey upon mice.

hat, āge, cāre, fär; let, bē, tėrm; it, īce; hot, ōpen, ôrder; oil, out; cup, pút, rüle, ūse; takən

pro ceed (prə sēd′),   1. move forward. The train proceeded at the same speed as before. 2. carry on any act. The man proceeded to light his pipe.

prop er (prop′ər), correct; right; fitting. Night is the proper time to sleep, and bed the proper place.

prop er ly (prop′ər li),   in a proper, correct, or fitting manner. Eat properly.

prove (prüv), 1. show that something is true or right. Prove these answers. 2. turn out; be found to be. The book proved interesting.

prowl (proul), go about slowly and secretly, hunting for something to eat or steal. Many wild animals prowl at night.

pur sue (pər sü′), chase. The policeman pursued the robbers.

pur su er (pər sü′ər), one who pursues.

quake (kwāk), 1. shake; tremble. The young girl quaked with fear. 2. a shaking; a trembling.

rang er (rān′jər), person employed to guard a forest region.

rap ture (rap′chər), very great joy. The mother gazed with rapture at her long-lost son.

rare[1] (rãr), 1. unusual; not usually found; not happening often. Snowstorms are rare in some parts of the country. 2. unusually good. Edison had rare powers as an inventor.

rare[2] (rãr), not cooked much; as, a rare piece of meat.

rare ly (rãr′li), not often.

realm (relm),   1. kingdom. 2. region.

reck on (rek′ən), 1. count; find the number or value of. You must reckon the cost before you decide. 2. consider; judge. He is reckoned the best player on the team. 3. think. The man said, "I reckon it's going to rain."

re cov er (ri kuv′ər), 1. get back (something lost, taken away, or stolen); as, to recover a purse. 2. get well. Ann is recovering from a long illness. 3. get over. The boy quickly recovered from his fright.

reed (rēd), a kind of tall grass with a hollow stalk that grows in wet places.

re gard (ri gärd′), look at; watch. The cat regarded me anxiously when I picked up her kittens. 2. a look; a steady look. The man's regard seemed fixed upon some distant object. 3. consider; think of. He is regarded as the best doctor in town.

re gion (rē′jən),   space; place; part of the world.

re late (ri lāt′), tell; report. The traveler related his adventures. 2. connect in thought or meaning. *Better* and *best* are related to *good*. 3. **Be related** sometimes means belong to the same family. Cousins are related.

re lief (ri lēf′), freedom from pain, worry, or difficulty.

re new (ri nü′ or ri nū′), 1. make new or strong again; make like new. 2. begin again. He renewed his efforts to open the window.

re quire (ri kwȋr′), 1. need. We require more spoons for our party. 2. demand; order; command. The rules required us all to be present.

risk (risk), 1. chance of harm or loss; danger. He rescued the dog at the risk of his own life. If you drive carefully, there is no risk of being fined. 2. take the risk of. The children risked drowning when they swam in the deep river.

roam (rōm), 1. wander; go about with no special plan or aim; as, to roam the forest.

rus tle (rus′əl), 1. sound that leaves make when moved by the wind; sound like this. 2. move so as to make such a sound. Her silk dress rustled when she walked. 3. move or stir (something) so that it makes such a sound; as, to rustle the papers.

sap[1] (sap), life-giving juice of a plant. Maple sugar is made from the sap of some maple trees.

sap[2] (sap), weaken; use up. The extreme heat sapped her strength.

scorch (skôrch), 1. burn slightly; burn on the outside. The fire scorched the boys' faces. 2. slight burn.

scorn ful (skôrn′fəl), making fun of; mocking. He spoke of our old car in a scornful voice.

se cure (si kūr′), 1. safe. This is a secure hiding place. 2. firm. Are the boards of this bridge secure? 3. get; obtain. We have secured our tickets for the school play.

sense (sens), 1. understanding, intelligence. He hasn't sense enough to come in when it rains. 2. feel; understand. Mother sensed that Father was tired.

shal low (shal′ō), not deep; as, shallow water, a shallow dish, a shallow mind.

shove (shuv), push. The people shoved to get on the crowded car. Tom gave the boat a shove which sent it far out into the water.

slash (slash), 1. cut with a sweeping stroke of a sword, knife, whip, or ax. 2. make a slashing stroke.

slight (slȋt), small; not much. I have a slight headache.

slope (slōp), 1. go up or down as shown in the picture. The land slopes toward the sea. The house has a sloping roof. 2. any surface, line, or land that goes up or down from a level. If you roll a ball up a slope, it will roll down again.

Slope of a hill

sneer (snēr), make fun of or mock by looks or words. The mean girls sneered at poor Jane's clothes.

snout (snout), long nose of an animal; the nose and mouth of an animal; as, the snout of a pig.

---

hat, āge, căre, fär; let, bē, tėrm; it, ȋce; hot, ōpen, ôrder; oil, out; cup, pu̇t, rüle, ūse; takən

sol emn (sol′əm), serious; earnest. He gave his solemn promise never to return.

sol id (sol′id), 1. hard; firm; strongly put together. They were glad to leave the boat and put their feet on solid ground. 2. alike throughout. The ring was solid gold.

sought (sôt), 1. looked for; hunted. For days she sought a safe hiding place. 2. tried. The bird sought to escape from the cage.

span gle (spang′gəl), sprinkle with small bright bits. The sky is spangled with stars.

spir it (spir′it), 1. supernatural being. God is a spirit. 2. state of mind. He is in good spirits. **Out of spirits** means sad; gloomy.

spout (spout), 1. flow out with force. Water spouted from the break in the pipe. 2. stream. A spout of water shot up from a hole in the pipe. 3. tube or lip by which liquid is poured. A teapot has a spout.

SPOUT

squaw (skwô), American Indian woman or wife.

steed (stēd), horse; war horse; riding horse.

strut (strut), walk in a vain, important way. The rooster struts about the barnyard.

stur dy (stėr′di), strong. Tom was small for his age but very sturdy.

suck er (suk′ər), part of an animal that is used for sucking or holding fast to things.

sur vey (sər vā′ for 1, sėr′vā for 2), 1. measure for size, shape, place, boundaries, etc. Men are surveying the land before it is divided into house lots. 2. careful measurement. Surveys showed that the northern boundary was not correct.

sur vey ing (sər vā′ing), the act or business of making surveys of land.

sur vey or (sər vā′ər), person who surveys.

sus pect (səs pekt′ for 1 and 2, sus′pekt for 3), 1. imagine to be so; think likely. The mouse suspected danger and did not touch the trap. I suspect that some accident has delayed him. 2. doubt. 3. person suspected.

swamp (swomp), wet, soft land.

swan (swon), large, graceful water bird with a long, slender, curving neck.

Swan (nearly 5 ft. long with the head and neck)

swarm (swôrm), 1. large group of insects flying or moving about together. 2. fly or move in great numbers. The flies swarmed about us.

swirl (swėrl), move with a twisting motion; whirl; as, dust swirling in the air.

swoop (swüp), come down with a rush, as a hawk does; sweep rapidly down upon.

syr up (sir′əp or sėr′əp), a thick, sweet liquid. Maple syrup is made from the sap of maple trees.

te di ous (tē′di əs or tē′jəs), long and tiring. A long talk that you cannot understand is tedious.

tem per a ture (tem′pər ə chər), degree of heat or cold. The temperature of freezing water is 32 degrees. The temperature of a person with fever is over 98½ degrees.

ter ror (ter′ər), great fear. The child has a terror of thunder.

thith er (thiŦH′ər), there.

threat en (thret′ən), 1. say what will be done to punish or harm. The farmer threatened to shoot any dog that killed one of his sheep. 2. give warning of coming trouble. The clouds threaten rain. 3. be a cause of possible harm to. A flood threatened the city.

throng (thrông), crowd. Great throngs of people came to see the President.

thun der bolt (thun′dər bōlt′), 1. flash of lightning and the thunder that follows it. 2. something sudden, startling, and terrifying.

toil (toil), 1. hard work. 2. work hard.

tor na do (tôr nā′dō), violent whirlwind that often destroys things.

tri al (trī′əl), trying or testing. He gave the machine another trial to see if it would work.

tribe (trīb), group of people living together under the same leaders. America was once the home of many tribes of Indians.

tri umph (trī′umf), joy because of victory or success. He took home his prize in triumph.

trout (trout), fresh-water food fish.

truce (trüs), a stop in fighting; peace for a short time. A truce was declared between the armies.

tu pe lo (tü′pə lō), large North American tree with strong, tough wood.

un der take (un′dər tāk′), 1. try; attempt. 2. agree to do; promise.

vain (vān), 1. having too much pride. She is vain of her beauty. 2. of no use; unsuccessful. She made vain attempts to reach her mother on the telephone. 3. **In vain** means without success. The drowning man shouted in vain, for no one could hear him.

val ley (val′i), 1. low land between hills or mountains. Most large valleys have rivers running through them. 2. wide region drained by a great river; as, the Ohio valley.

ven ture (ven′chər), 1. dare. No one ventured to interrupt the speaker. 2. dare to say, go, make, or try something. In spite of the storm, the boys ventured outside.

vi o lent (vī′ə lənt), 1. rough; forceful; as, a violent blow. 2. showing or caused by very strong feeling or action; as, violent language, a violent war.

---

hat, āge, cãre, fär; let, bē, tèrm; it, īce; hot, ōpen, ôrder; oil, out; cup, pùt, rüle, ūse; takən

vi o lent ly (vī′ə lənt li),   in a violent way.

vow (vou),   1. solemn promise. 2. declare earnestly or forcefully. She vowed never to leave home again.

wal low (wol′ō),   1. roll about. The pigs wallowed in the mud. 2. place where an animal wallows.

weap on (wep′ən),   thing used in fighting or attacking. Swords, arrows, clubs, guns, claws, horns, teeth, and stings are weapons.

wea sel (wē′zəl),   small animal with a slim body, that eats rats, mice, birds, and other small animals.

Weasel (6 to 8 in. long without the tail)

wedge (wej),   1. something shaped like the letter V.   2. thrust or pack in tight. He wedged himself through the narrow window. The man's foot was wedged between the rocks, so that he could not get away.

whin ny (hwin′i), 1. sound that a horse makes.   2. make such a sound.

wick (wik),   the part of an oil lamp, candle, or torch that is lighted.

wig wam (wig′wom),   hut of poles covered with bark, mats, or skins, made by American Indians.

Candle cut to show the wick

wil der ness (wil′dər nis),   wild place; region with few or no people living in it.

wisp (wisp),   1. small bunch; as, a wisp of hair.   2. little thing; as, a wisp of a girl.

wit (wit),   understanding; mind; sense.   People with quick wits learn easily.   The child was out of his wits with fright.

with er (wiᴛH′ər),   dry up; wrinkle.   Flowers wither after they are cut.   Age had withered the old woman's face.

wit ty (wit′i),   amusing and clever.   He makes witty remarks.

---

hat, āge, cāre, fär;   let, bē, tėrm;   it, īce;   hot, ōpen, ôrder;   oil, out; cup, pút, rüle, ūse;   takən

TO THE TEACHER

More Times and Places, Book 4[2], with its accompanying *Guidebook* and *Think-and-Do Book*, continues The New Basic Reading Program for the middle grades. It is designed for approximately one semester's use whenever the child has successfully completed the new *Times and Places*.

More Times and Places contains 513 words not introduced by the end of Book 4[1] of The New Basic Reading Program. Each of these new words is used four or more times in this book, and there is a maximum of four new words to a page. The majority of words introduced in the new *Times and Places* are further repeated in *More Times and Places*.

The 513 new words in this book are listed below. The following forms of known words are not counted as new (including those forms made by changing *y* to *i* or *f* to *v*, dropping the final *e*, or doubling the final consonant in the root word): forms made by adding or dropping the inflectional endings *s*, *es*, *ed*, *ing*, *n*, *en*, and *er*, *est* of comparison; possessives; forms made by adding or dropping the prefixes *dis-*, *im-*, *re-*, or *un-* and the suffixes *-en*, *-er*, *-ful*, *-ish*, *-less*, *-ly*, *-ness*, or *-y*, and *-teen*, *-th*, or *-ty* of numerals; compounds made up of known words; contractions. Also, homographs are not counted as separate words; for example, if *fleet* meaning "ships under one command" has been introduced, *fleet* meaning "fast moving or rapid" is not counted as a separate word. Nonsense words as well as syllables that represent sounds are not counted as new.

The red asterisks indicate 472 words that boys and girls can attack independently by applying the word-attack skills developed in The New Basic Reading Program and by using the pronunciations in the glossary of *More Times and Places*. Those starred words printed in italics in the vocabulary list are defined in the glossary. The type of analysis that pupils can use in unlocking each attack word is indicated in the *Guidebook* for *More Times and Places*.

VOCABULARY LIST

UNIT I

	13 *frequently* *	20 *linger* *	26 rattlesnake *
	capture *	21 *apparently* *	27 grasped *
6 *brilliant* *	14 ruined	22 *swamps* *	defends *
7 *crabs* *	15 *cactus* *	Santee *	28 *panic* *
shallow *	*mesquite* *	*alligator* *	29 *lunged* *
motionless *	duties *	*coiled* *	30 *peered* *
8 sweater	provide *	23 'gator *	dimness *
9 guided *	16 ornaments *	encouraged *	*convinced* *
securely *	bitterly *	24 *cypress* *	31 St.
argued *	forehead	moss *	Louis
10 lap *	17 youngsters	blossoms *	32 sped *
11 vacant *	quarter	*tupelo* *	*region* *
12 moaning *	18	25 hollow *	*tornado* *
meanwhile *	19	coon *	

315

33 curved *
 syrup *
34 ceased *
 western *
35 *hesitate* *
36 *slashing* *
37 . . . . .
38 Vermont *
 Jason *
 sap *
39 buckets *
 lonesome *
40 *boring* *
 spout *
41 tank *
 pipe *
 recognized
42 gallons *
43 bubbles *
 violently *
44 pitcher *
 containing *
45 . . . . .
46 *arrival* *
47 Stephen
 railroad *
 valley *
48 season *
49 . . . . .
50 *slope* *
 level *
 peaceful *
51 *fossil* *
 familiar *
 grizzly *
52 buried *
 rumble *
53 . . . . .
54 receiver *
55 . . . . .
56 southern
 California

57 *temperature* *
 freezing *
 orchard *
 belt *
58 comforting
 oil *
 lit *
 torch *
59 *wick* *
60 choking *
 throat *
 relief *
61 boomed *
62 *double* *
63 northern *
 Antoine
 November *
 papa *
64 Ace *
 supply *
 lumber *
 pine *
65 message *
66 *dusk* *
67 Chalmers *
68 whom *
69 *wilderness* *
70 . . . . .
71 praised *
72 *canyon* *
 Howard
73 *trout* *
 rod *
 permit *
74 *permission* *
 crickets *
75 *proved* *
 dainty *
76 *ranger* *
 timber *
 patrol *
77 . . . . .
78 fought *
 desperately *

79 . . . . .
80 *scorched* *

UNIT II

81 . . . . .
82 *advancing* *
83 skunk *
 insects *
 deserves *
84 *occasionally* *
 paused *
85 *slight* *
 movement *
86 *gradually* *
 fleeing *
 swooped *
87 slim *
 keen *
88 twitched *
 bolted *
89 . . . . .
90 war
 forefeet *
91 partner *
 gully *
 whinny *
 pounce *
92 cliff *
 fury *
 terror *
 crafty *
93 injured *
 intent *
 prey *
 rescue *
94 *enraged* *
 mare *
 gleamed *
95 splendid *
 downward *
96 distant *
 pity *

97 . . . . .
98 *risk* *
 passageway *
 directly *
99 knelt *
100 . . . . .
101 encircled *
 glimpse *
102 *midsummer* *
 ventured *
 weasels *
 prowled *
103 *dread* *
104 sneaking *
 fled *
105 . . . . .
106 force *
 greedy *
 roots *
 increased *
107 *rustling* *
108 *loons* *
 companion *
109 . . . . .
110 . . . . .
111 lantern *
112 upward *
 dawn *
 mist *
 swirling *
113 *opposite* *
114 lane *
 foam *
115 eagle *
116 forepaws *
 chose *
 considered *
 roamed *
117 solid *
118 *alert* *
 Husky *
 heeding *
119 anger *
 sensed *

316

120 swallowed *
nature *
ambled *
121 tawny *
pitched *
purred *
122 Leone's
ledge *
shove *
humped *
123 butterfly *
crouched *
coyote *
124 hissed *
uttering *
125 *despair* *
threatened *
126 *confused* *
127 . . . . .
128 Willie *
Herbert *
129 *determined* *
concern *
130 attending *
Charlie *
flapjacks *
131 flung *
132 freedom *
skillfully *
133 *overcome* *
appearance *
134 . . . . .
135 *strutted* *
136 *glossy* *
cove *
137 *brief* *
recovered *
138 gliding *
139 forbidden *
snout *
140 *pierce* *
faltered *
141 *suckers* *

142 *octopus* *
143 Nika
wedge *
southward *
gander *
144 rays *
145 rice *
concealed *
reeds *
146 . . . . .
147 *drake* *
148 fowls *
vain *
149 Frank *
Gordon *
Lizzie *
faithful *
150 . . . . .
151 . . . . .
152 *harsh* *
blasts *

UNIT III

153 famous *
Americans
154 *tedious* *
155 *surveying* *
boundary *
156 Lawrence
Vernon *
future *
England
157 *surveyor* *
Byrne
158 tramping *
159 describe *
160 William *
Fairfax *
lord *
accompany *
161 Virginia

162 *abroad* *
163 Daniel
Boone *
reckon *
drawled *
164 rifle *
weapon *
slender *
165 *opportunity* *
166 absent *
167 *plume* *
168 *midst* *
169 *dreary* *
170 invitation *
taffy *
Noah
Webster *
171 *odor* *
Rebecca *
Jerusha *
172 manner *
173 *audience* *
174 *departed* *
arithmetic *
Bible *
wits *
175 . . . . .
176 Fulton's *
folly *
Christopher
177 . . . . .
178 speechless *
invented *
crank *
179 invention *
ship *
180 France *
renewed *
attacked *
jeered *
181 *completion* *
tested *

182 *throngs* *
deck *
183 *triumph* *
echoing *
184 Baltimore *
Pickersgill *
regarded *
banner *
185 Francis *
Scott *
spangled *
186 prisoners
Dr. *
truce *
fleet *
187 battle *
bomb *
188 tune *
189 pigeon
Indiana
Abraham *
Lincoln *
190 *sturdy* *
youth
Abe *
191 illness *
community *
death *
192 *fodder* *
193 . . . . .
194 honest
combing *
toiled *
195 entertain *
196 Taylor *
occurred *
Barnum *
exhibiting *
197 amusement *
198 collection *
museum *
attract *

318

ACKNOWLEDGMENTS

For permission to adapt and use copyrighted material, grateful acknowledgment is made to the following:

To the author and publishers for "Unwelcome Passengers," adapted from *Penny and Peter* by Carolyn Haywood, copyright, 1946, by Harcourt, Brace and Company, Inc.; to the author for "A Christmas to Remember" by Catherine Blanton in *American Junior Red Cross News;* to the publishers for "Adventure in the Swamps" from "The Alligator's Tail" by Idella Purnell, copyright, 1938, by Story Parade, Inc., reprinted by permission; to the author for "Judy's Chickens" from "Rosina's Chickens" and for "Maple-Sugar Time" from "Maple Sugar Surprise" by Gladys Relyea Saxon in *American Junior Red Cross News;* to the author and publishers for "Alarm in the Night" by Fleur Conkling in *Children's Activities;* to the author and publishers for "The School Train" from *The School Train* by Helen Acker, published by Abelard Press, Inc.; to Mrs. Graham Doar for "A Camp in the Canyon" from "Fires Start in the Fall" by Eleanor Hammond in *Junior World.*

To the author for "Zoo Without Bars" by Garald Lagard in *American Childhood;* to the author and publishers for "A Falls and a Fawn" by Dorothy Dill Mason in *Trails for Juniors;* to the publishers for "Bushy Tail's Escape" from *Bushy Tail* by Alice Crew Gall and Fleming Crew, copyright, 1941, by Oxford University Press, Inc.; to the publishers for "Billy and the Loons" by Laura E. Wiggins, copyright, 1950, by Story Parade, Inc., reprinted by permission; to the publishers for "Wilderness Partners" from *Snow Dog* by Jim Kjelgaard, published by Holiday House; to the author for "The Magic Coat" from *Tawny Goes Hunting* by Allen Chaffee, published by Random House, Inc.; to Lantern Press, Inc., for "Willie the Moose" from *Young Readers Animal Stories*, copyright, 1950, by Adolph Regli; to the author and publishers for "Gray Wing and Nika" from "In the Wake of the Storm" by William H. Bunce in *Trails.*

To the author and publishers for "George Grows Up" from *George Washington, Leader of the People* by Clara Ingram Judson, published by Wilcox & Follett Company; to the publishers for "The Boy Hunter" by Clarence M. Lindsay, copyright, 1949, by Story Parade, Inc., reprinted by permission; to the author and publishers for "The Spelling Bee," adapted from *Homespun Playdays* by Carolyn Sherwin Bailey, copyright, 1941, by Carolyn Sherwin Bailey, reprinted by permission of The Viking Press, Inc., New York; to the author for "How a Song Named a Flag" by Fannie R. Buchanan in *Story Parade;* to the author for "A Boy and His Book" from "A Little Lad of Long Ago" by Alice E. Allen in *Good Housekeeping;* to the author and publishers for "A Great Showman" from *The Boy's Life of Barnum* by Harvey W. Root, published by Harper & Brothers; to the author for "Nothing for Herself" from *The Story of Clara Barton of the Red Cross* by Jeannette Covert Nolan, published by Julian Messner, Inc.; to the author and publishers for "Night Is Turned into Day" from *The Story of Thomas Alva Edison* by Enid La Monte Meadowcroft, Grosset & Dunlap Signature Books, 1952.

To Mrs. Clifton Johnson for "The Four Musicians" from *The Oak Tree Fairy Book*, edited by Clifton Johnson, copyright, 1933; to the publisher for "Tyll's Masterpiece" from *Tyll Ulenspiegel's Merry Pranks* by M. Jagendorf, copyright, 1938, by Vanguard Press, Inc., used by permission of the publisher; to James B. Pinker and Son, Inc., Agents, for "Rumpelstiltskin" from *Told Again* by Walter de la Mare.

ILLUSTRATIONS

The pictures in this book were made by Seymour Fleishman (cover, pp. 1, 175, 249-253); Henry M. Picken (pp. 2-3, 38-55, 63-71, 82-89, 108-126); Brinton Turkle (pp. 5, 14-21, 56-62, 81, 153, 219); Fred Scott-Wood (pp. 6-12, 30-36, 95-100); John Merryweather (pp. 22-28, 90-93, 169-173, 189-209); I. Heilbron (pp. 72-79, 267, 274, 278, 290); Earl Sherwan (pp. 102-107, 136-141); Willard Arnold (pp. 128-135, 220-226, 270, 277); L. M. Henderson (pp. 143-152); Raymon Naylor (pp. 154-168, 176-187, 211-218); Mary Gehr (pp. 232-238); Nell Smock (pp. 240-248); Keith Ward (pp. 228-231, 256-265); E. Segner (pp. 268-269, 272-273, 276); Milo Winter (pp. 280-281, 285-288).

THE NEW BASIC READERS

CURRICULUM FOUNDATION SERIES

REG U.S PAT. OFF